## AUTHOR'S INTRODUCTION

"Aladdin And The Blue Genie" is a joyous pantomime, packed with adventure, songs and laughter. It is unprotected and royalty free. Directors can feel free to make any amendments or changes they wish (apart from the title please!) Additional copies can be obtained from the author, or it is entirely acceptable to obtain your own.

The author does not wish to receive any remuneration for this pantomime, however, if you wish to make a donation to the 'Children With Cancer' charity that would be very kind, but be purely voluntary on your part.

Publisher:   Independent Publishing Network
Publication date:  June 2021
ISBN:   978-1-80049-702-3
Author:   Joan R. Blumire
Email:   j.blumire@outlook.com
Please direct all enquiries to the author

## MUSIC

The songs, lyrics, parodies, have been carefully chosen to be an integral part of the script. Hopefully all, or most, can remain, particularly the last two songs, acting as a powerful finale. Most of the songs were released and/or published prior to 1970, with a few exceptions. A full music list is given at the end.

For any copyright music it is your responsibility to ensure any royalties arising from its performance are paid. The Performing Rights Society (PRS) licences the use of and collects Royalties for the vast majority of popular music.

For the avoidance of doubt, any music or lyrics in this script does not imply permission has been granted for its use (or royalties paid) and users of this script are hereby advised to make their own arrangements.

## SCENERY/STAGE DIRECTIONS

Few instructions have been given, and these can be ignored and left to your discretion.

## LIGHTING/SOUND EFFECTS

Again, only minimal suggestions, you are again invited to use your expertise, using facilities available.

## COSTUMES

An important part of any pantomime, it is hoped you will do your best to obtain appropriate costumes, particularly the 'ferocious animal' costumes. It will delight the children and keep them coming back for your next show!

## AUDIENCE PARTICIPATION

There are many instances in the songs and general script where it will be fun for the children and general audience to join in. You can feel entirely free to go 'off script' in order to better encourage their participation.

Excalibur is a legendary sword, sometimes attributed with magical powers. The sword could not be released from the stone except by the true king.

"Whoso pulleth out this sword of this stone is rightwise king born"

(Sir Thomas Mallory's 'Morte D'Arthur' 1469)

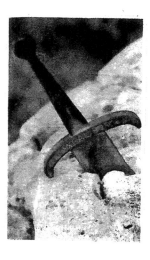

ACTORS' NOTES

Becoming 'Frozen'

Hopefully there will be a thunder clap and/or a clash of cymbals and a flash of light. At that point the actors could swing around so their backs are to the audience as though startled by the light and/or sound. This should make it easier to stay in position when Brazzadin shouts "Freeze!"

Moonwalking

Some actors will be required to 'moonwalk.' It is suggested you google: How To Moonwalk, (Dance Moves Tutorial) Mihran Kirakosian. Come on, everybody, make Michael proud!

Dance Instruction

Widow Twankey and Willie Washee will need to google "The Secrets of Russian Pas De Deux" click Sneak Preview - Youtube (no lifts, just steadying by Willie W., no hernias!)

Singing

All the songs can be 'googled.' Do look them up and become familiar with the music and the beat. Note which lyrics have stayed the same and which have been altered. Play the songs over again until they become 'old friends.'

This is a pantomime, not an opera. If you happen to be an accomplished singer, that is wonderful, but the author feels the important thing is for the words to be clearly audible and the songs to be sung with enormous enthusiasm. It is time to lose your inhibitions, and a great sense of humour will help, so if you've never even sung in the shower, don't let that stop you participating. You are here to give the audience a great time, an unforgettable evening, and, oh yes, have a great time yourself!

# ALADDIN AND THE BLUE GENIE

## ACT 1    Scene 1

Street Scene and Widow Twankey's laundry near Peking, China

## ACT 1    Scene 2

Somewhere in The Arabian desert

## ACT 2    Scene 1

In The Cave Of Brazzadin

## ACT 2    Scene 2

In The Emperor's Palace - a traditional Chinese Wedding

As a royalty free, unprotected script, this allows you to make any changes to the script you wish, without permission from the author, (well, anything but the title!)  What's not to like!

CHARACTERS    In order of appearance

| | |
|---|---|
| ALADDIN: | A romantic dreamer, with his head in the clouds. |
| WILLIE WASHEE: | A loyal friend to Aladdin, but lacking courage. |
| LAUNDRY WORKERS: | Employees of Widow Twankey. |
| PRIMROSE : | Clumsy, shy, but sweet and lovable. |
| WIDOW TWANKEY: | 'Over the top' panto character. |
| BRAZZADIN: | Every panto has an evil magician, so he is ours! |
| THE EMPEROR: | An overbearing, comic character, who needs a good woman to put him in his place. Father to Princess Jasmine. |
| PRINCESS JASMINE: | A lovely princess. |
| COLUMBINE: | An attractive handmaiden to the Princess. |
| TRAMP (AL): | A tramp down on his luck, a victim of the system. |
| LENNY & HENDY: | Two policemen of the old Music Hall variety type. |
| BLUE GENIE: | A bumbling character whose genie powers leave a lot to be desired. (but you've really got to love him!) |
| PUFFLEY: | A female dragon, aware of her sensuality. |
| BIZZIE LIZZIE: | A female bee, aware of her sensuality. |
| TEDDY: | A male bear, more than a little fond of Bizzy Lizzie. |
| LEOPOLD: | A male lion, more than a little fond of Puffley. |
| PHINEAS FUNGUS: | A male skeleton. |
| MAUDIE MAGGOT | A female mummy. |
| CALEB CARBUNCLE: | Cave creatures of your choice. |
| DAPHNE DYSENTERY: | - " - |
| STANLEY STAGNACIOUS: | - " - |
| PRISCILLA PESTILENCE: | - " - |
| SCABIES SALMONELLA: | female skeleton |
| HERALD : | |

There is a lot of scope for an actor to play more than one part. Possibilities might be:
Laundry workers /Lenny & Hendy , 'ferocious' animals/cave creatures
 Laundry workers/Tramp/Herald
Primrose/'ferocious' animal
Male/female actor roles can be interchanged in many instances. (All part of panto fun, not to be taken too seriously!)

On the other hand if choruses are required, they can be added to laundry workers, all characters in Act 1, Scenes 1 and 2, and to the cave creatures in Act 2, Scenes 1 and 2.

# ALADDIN AND THE BLUE GENIE

## ACT 1    Scene 1

The scene is a street near the ancient city of Peking, in China, with open interior of Widow Twankey's laundry extending outwards on the street with a table or counter containing the props needed for the scene. There should be a simple wooden chair at the rear of the stage. It would be an advantage if there were other items suggesting a laundry, i.e. baskets containing clothes, fake washing machine, mangle, washboards, a filled clothes line, would all be possibilities.

M U S I C # 1  "Land Of China"

Musical overture continues as background music while curtains open and we see laundry workers and Aladdin and Willie Washee standing idly about chatting, Willie leaning on a mop. The music only stops, when Willie, peering towards SL opening, sees Widow Twankey advancing.

WILLIE W:    Look out, everybody, Widow Twankey's coming!

(everybody panics as they hastily run around to get to their places, bumping into each other, tripping and only just about managing to get to their places as Widow T. makes a grand entrance, carrying aloft a long, thin, loaf of bread.)

WIDOW T:    Packed.....Packed, I tell you! Never seen so many idiots shopping in the market place, and so rude! Had to elbow them out of the way (mimes vicious elbow jabbing and hip pushing) to grab the last piece of stale bread for your Sunday dinner!

('spits' on the bread and rubs it with her sleeve) A few lumps of mouldy green stuff won't hurt no-one, just adds to the flavour.

Well, don't just stand about, you've got work to do. You'd better start to scrub if you want any grub. (looks at audience) And look at all those customers sitting out there waiting for us to wash their dirty underwear!

What about you, sir? (to man in audience) Take off your dirty knickers and we'll give them a lovely wash and spin dry.

Pooh! (to man in audience) Your socks smell a bit! They need a good scrub! We can give you a good price this week - one for 60P or we'll do the pair for 80P each.

(to woman in audience) Is that a white bra you're wearing? Didn't anyone tell you white is out of fashion this year? Take it off, I'll put it in our late model washing machine and it'll come out a lovely shade of dirty grey!

ALADDIN:  (pulling at W.T.'s sleeve) No ma, they've come to see the pantomime.

WIDOW T:  Pantomime, what pantomime, Aladdin? I'm too busy for such foolishness. I've got to iron my smalls.

WILLIE W:  (distressed) They've bought tickets and programmes and everything. Some of them even brushed their teeth and scrubbed under their arms.

WIDOW T:  (looking at audience) Raise your hands if you've tickets. Those of you who haven't got their hands raised, so haven't got tickets, please leave by the rear exit.

Ok you can stay, put your hands down and stop waving them about at me!

I suppose we'd better put on a show for all of you. How about "Godzilla Eats The ( local ) Library?" I can't hear you! (cups hand to ear)

EVERYONE:  NO!

WIDOW T:  How about "The Monster Who Ate The ( local ) Theatre?" I can't hear you! (cups hand to ear).

EVERYONE:  NO!

WIDOW T:  I think this audience is looking for something more classical. Very well, I shall perform my infamous Pas De Deux (pronouncing Pass Dee Ducks) from "Swan Lake Ballet" Come here Willie Washee. (drags him behind her)

M U S I C # 2  "Swan Lake Ballet Music - Dance Of The Swans"

(They now perform a Pas De Deux and additional steps in a serious manner, being much funnier than merely waving arms about. (steadying, no lifting by Willie W. — no hernias!)

WIDOW T:  That was impressive, wasn't it folks? How would you like to watch that for the next two and a half hours?

EVERYONE:  NO!

ALADDIN:  They want us to do "Aladdin And The Blue Genie."

WIDOW T:  Oh, alright, I'll be the star, and you and Willie can play small parts.

ALADDIN:  I want to fall in love with a beautiful princess.

WILLIE W:  Foolish boy, you wouldn't know what to do with a princess if you had one.

ALADDIN:     I want a princess!  I want a princess!  (stamping foot)

WIDOW T:     Oh, ok Aladdin, you can have a beautiful princess, but don't blame me if she tosses you aside after she finds out you are just a simple washerwoman's son.

WILLIE W:     No fair, he always gets everything he wants.  If he gets a beautiful princess I want a beautiful handmaiden!

WIDOW T:     You can't have everything you want.  You'll be too busy mopping laundry room floors.  I don't pay you almost minimum wage so you can stand there dreaming of handmaidens.

          (Willie bursts into tears)

WILLIE W:     I want a handmaiden!  I want a handmaiden!

WIDOW T:     Stop blubbering Willie Washee, you can have your silly handmaiden.

          (Willie stops crying instantly, jumps up and down, clapping his hands with glee)

LDRY WKRS:     Me!  Me!  Me!

WIDOW T:     Might have known you lot would want to be in it.  You can do it on your own time,  I'm not going to pay you overtime.  How many of you are there?  One, two, three , (etc.)  Someone's missing.  Primrose!  Where is that silly girl?  Primrose!

          (Primrose comes out shyly from behind the others, promptly dropping a tin bowl (or similar) As she attempts to pick it up she drops another, then another, becoming ever more flustered and bumping into people trying to help her).

PRIMROSE:     (very tearful and agitated) I'm sorry Widow Twankey, I didn't mean to, I get so flustered, I won't do it again, I'll try harder.

WIDOW T:     Foolish girl (to audience) Not to worry, I'm planning to sack her at the end of the pantomime.

ALADDIN:     We should have some happy policemen, a miserable tramp and an Emperor.

WILLIE W.     And big ferocious animals, ghosts and ghoulies and scary things that go boo!

WIDOW T:     We don't want ghosts, ghoulies and scary things that go boo.  They will frighten the children. (to audience)  Anyone wants things that go boo? (cupping hand to ear).

WILLIE W:     See, that boy over here wants scary things.

ALADDIN:     And that boy over there.

WIDOW T:    Oh, well children, it's your pantomime, we'll have big ferocious animals and ghosts and ghoulies and scary things if that's what you want.

ALADDIN:    Ooooh! Ooooh! Ooooh!  I know, we've got to have a Blue Genie!

WIDOW T:    No way, have you any idea of the price of Blue Genies these days?  You can't get one in the market for less than 60P an hour.

ALADDIN:    We've got to have one, the pantomime is called "Aladdin And The Blue Genie" (to audience) Tell Widow Twankey, We want a Blue Genie!  We want a Blue Genie! (cups hand to ear)

EVERYONE:    We want a Blue Genie!  We want a Blue Genie!

WIDOW T:    (to audience)  Oh well, I'll see what I can do children, but I'm not making any promises, we'll just have to wait and see if a Blue Genie  suddenly appears.  One thing you can be very sure of, there will be no Evil Magicians stomping around, casting evil spells all over the place. You agree with that children, don't you, no Evil Magicians in our pantomime? (cups hand to ear)  Let's hear you say it, "No Evil Magicians!  No Evil Magicians!

EVERYONE:    No Evil Magicians!  No Evil Magicians!

WIDOW T:    That's very good, children, now we're going to .......

(sound of distant thunder)

Did you hear that thunder, children?  Funny, I thought it wasn't supposed to rain today. As I was saying, your pantomime is definitely and decidedly not going to have an Evil Magician stomping around and casting his evil spells over.....

(crash of thunder and/or cymbals/flash of light. Lights could go out for 2 or 3 seconds to allow for Brazzadin to come on stage, entering from SL)

(everyone, startled, by the noise/light, jumps and turns away from audience)

BRAZZADIN:    FREEZE!  (everyone 'freezes')  BACK, BACK, I tell you!  (everyone 'moonwalks' back towards SR, some moving in rather a zig zag direction, (letting them to show off their 'moonwalking' skills!)  but allowing enough room for Brazzadin to come to centre stage)

SAUSAGES AND SNAKE SKINS! They think they are going to do a pantomime without me, do they? Me, Brazzadin, the world's most powerful and evil magician. I shall cast my evil spells and have them all in my power. Why do I do those evil things? Because I'm bad to the bone, that's right, I'm bad to the bone!

M U S I C # 3    "Bad To The Bone"

("You, Yours, Yours and yours alone, Tell ya Honey" are all opportunities to point to particular ladies in the audience).

> Now on the day I was born
> The nurses all gathered 'round
> And they gazed in wide wonder
> At the joy they had found.
> The head nurse spoke up
> Said "leave this one alone"
> She could tell right away
> That I was bad to the bone
>
> Bad to the bone
> Bad to the bone
> I'm evil and bad
> I make everyone mad
> They call me a cad
> Bad to the bone
>
> I broke a thousand hearts
> Before I met you;
> I'll break a thousand more baby
> Before I am through
> I wanna be yours pretty baby
> Yours and yours alone,
> I'm here to tell ya honey
> That I'm bad to the bone.

Now I shall go and hide myself away, but never fear, I'll come back another day, and when I do, the earth will shake because of the evil spells that I will make. They'll be sorry they shut me out. I'll spoil their fun, you can have no doubt!

(he stalks off in high dudgeon. Everyone starts to wake up, looking dazed for a few moments, stumbling around a little before returning to normal).

WIDOW T:   Now what was I saying? Oh, yes, your panto is definitely and decidedly not going to have an Evil Magician stomping around and casting his evil spells over us. We don't want that, do we, children? No, of course not! If any evil Magician tries to come into your panto I will jump on his toes, and run him right off the stage. You can be sure of that!

Ok everyone, let's get this party started! Places everyone please! (everyone gets into position Widow T. turns her back to the audience) Are you ready? Are you steady? Go!

(holding her bread aloft, she conducts the cast members, using her loaf as a baton and enthusiastically keeping time with the beats (G: "Orchestra Conducting Fundamentals - Conducting Orchestra in 4/4))

MUSIC # 4 "In The Navy" Parody

EVERYONE:   In the laundry            (enthusiastically!)
            We are like the busy bees.
            In the laundry
            We have no time to sneeze.
            In the laundry! In the laundry!

WIDOW T:   No! No! No! That is no good at all. (to audience) I'm sorry everyone, I'm afraid you will have to help out. When I say "WHERE" I want you to sing "In the laundry! In the laundry! Can you do that? Let's give it a try. (cups hand to ear) "WHERE?"

EVERYONE:   In the laundry! In the laundry!

WIDOW T:   Am I going deaf? I couldn't hear that at all. Let's try again, but much louder!

(cups hand to ear)    WHERE?

EVERYONE:   In the laundry! In the laundry!

WIDOW T:   Oh, that's much better!

(Once again she turns her back to the audience, conducting with her bread, but turning and conducting audience for WHERE?! In the laundry! In the laundry!)

EVERYONE:    In the laundry
We are like the busy bees,
In the laundry
We have no time to sneeze   (W H E R E ? !)
IN THE LAUNDRY!  IN THE LAUNDRY!

In the laundry
We put knickers in the wash,
In the laundry
They're rinsed in orange squash!  (Lndry wrkrs hold up orange knickers)  (W H E R E ?!)
IN THE LAUNDRY!  IN THE LAUNDRY!

In the laundry
We hear the latest rumours
In the laundry
Widow Twankey's got red bloomers! (lndry wrkrs hold up red bloomers (W H E R E ?!)
IN THE LAUNDRY!   IN THE LAUNDRY!

In the laundry
The smell gets up your nose,
In the laundry
As the pile just grows and grows  (W H E R E ? !)
IN THE LAUNDRY!  IN THE LAUNDRY!

(W H E R E ?)  IN THE LAUNDRY!  (quieter)

(WHERE ?)  In the laundry (softly)

(W H E R E ? )  IN THE LAUNDRY!  (LOUDEST!!!)

(Widow T. could motion downwards with her hand to show quieter and softly)

WIDOW T:   (to audience) Well done, you are excellent singers. Well, you are loud anyway! Now I have something wonderful to tell you. Today is my birthday! Yes, today I am 52....... Whoops, I mean 22! You may sing "Happy Birthday" to me. (cups hand to ear)

EVERYONE:   "Happy birthday to you, happy birthday to you, happy birthday Widow Twankey, Happy birthday to you!"

WIDOW T:   Thank you, thank you. Now as you can see from my looks, I am in my prime.

EVERYONE:   (groans)

WIDOW T:   Yes, this is the prime of Miss Widow Twankey, and I have an exciting surprise for all the men in the audience. Today I am going to chose myself a husband. Yes, one lucky man in the audience is going to be my future husband. Husband number five or six I think, can't remember, I've lost count.

(pointing to a man in the audience) How about you sir, I bet you'd love to be Widow Twankey's next husband? A hot dinner every few weeks and a clean pair of underpants every month there is a Z in it.

(pointing to another man in the audience) How about you sir, I bet you'd love to share a marriage bed with Widow Twankey. Yes?

(pointing to another man in the audience) How about you, sir, with your brains and my looks, think what spectacular children we'll have!

        (sound of trumpets)

WIDOW T:   Trumpets, the sound of royal trumpets! That means the Emperor is coming!

        (more trumpets)

ALADDIN:   The princess is coming!

        (more trumpets)

WILLIE W:   The handmaiden is coming!

WIDOW T;   I've got to get ready, how do I look? Lucky I washed my hair last year. Are my knickers on straight?

        (bends over and audience gets to see her red bloomers)

Where's my lipstick? Bring me a mirror.

(laundry wrkrs bring her a large hand mirror and a lipstick. She puts on the bright red lipstick and looks at herself this way and that way in the mirror).

WIDOW T:   Mirror, mirror in my hand, who's the most gorgeous woman in the land? (pause) Cheeky!

M U S I C # 5   "I Feel Pretty"

(She should put the bread in her pocket, bra or hand it off to a laundry worker to put on the table, likewise lipstick, so she can dance around the stage holding the mirror aloft, singing).

I feel pretty
Oh so pretty,
I feel pretty and witty and bright!
And I pity
Any girl who isn't me tonight.

See that pretty girl in the mirror there
Who can that attractive girl be?
Such a pretty face
Such a pretty dress
Such a pretty smiile
Such a pretty me!

I feel stunning
And entrancing
Feel like running and dancing for joy
For I'm in love
With a pretty wonderful boy!

(There is a loud sound of trumpets. The Emperor enters, followed by Princess Jasmine and her handmaiden Columbine. They can be walking, or if facilities allow, be in a sedan chair, with curtain hiding feet, 'carried' by two slaves).

(As the Emperor enters, everyone, except Widow Twankey, bows by holding hands high above head and then bending from the waist. They remain in that position until the W.T. speech ending "hollering for your mummy.")

(The Emperor looks around imperiously and points his finger with outstretched arm at W.T)

EMPEROR:    Bow to Eggbert En-Jie Jingping, Emperor of Peking in China,  and all its surrounding districts!

WIDOW T:    Oh, you are a laugh Eggbert, all those airs and graces!

EMPEROR:     Do you understand when I speak to you, lowly unemancipated woman, only put on this earth to serve mankind for all his needs?  To cook and clean for him, to show him obedience and cater to his every whim!

EVERYONE:     (still bowing) Boo-oo-oo!

WIDOW T:     Oh don't be such a silly goose. I remember you in school when you were wearing short pants and wiping your runny nose on your sleeve. Remember that time when I crept up behind you, tickled you and shouted Boo! You wet your pants and started hollering for your mummy!

(everyone stands up and starts to laugh)

How's your bladder these days Eggbert, still tickleish are you?

(puts both her hands on his waist, tickling him)

Tickle, tickle!  Tickle, tickle!

(Emperor squirms around)

EMPEROR:     Ooh, eh, stop it, I'm losing my dignity!

WIDOW T:     Better than losing your pants!

Let's take a look at you. Hmm, not the greatest specimen of mankind, are you?  Never mind, I'm not too fussy.

EMPEROR:     Let me pass, woman!

        (tries to pass to her right -    she steps in front of him)
        (tries to pass to her left    -   she steps in front of him)
        (tries to pass to her right  -    she steps in front of him)

        (she feels his muscles)

WIDOW T:     Not been doing much working out at the gym lately have we?  Although (lifting up his arm and sniffing under his armpits) I must say you pong like you have. Smells like Gorgozola cheese under there.

EMPEROR:     Unhand me woman, how dare you touch my royal person!

WIDOW T:     Grab him, everybody!  Let's give his clothes a good scrub!

(Everyone converges upon him. (except for Princess Jasmine and Columbine, who just stand there laughing) They hold his arms at his side, while one pulls his baggy trousers down from the front).

(Another worker rushes to put a chair behind him. When pants are down, they 'push' him into the chair. He is struggling ineffectually throughout. As he sits on the chair his two legs go upward and they are able to remove his shoes. (which preferably are a slip-on type and come off easily) They can now completely remove his baggy trousers).

(The Emperor struggles and manages to stand up, and they now remove his upper garment. This should show an extraordinarily, hilariously decorated undershirt).

(The Emperor should be wearing a scarf affair which is tied around his neck, the ends hanging loosely in front. He should also be wearing headgear of a type deemed suitable).

(The Emperor should therefore now be standing wearing headgear, scarf, undershirt, boxer shorts and socks, and, if he can manage to put them on - shoes).

EMPEROR:     Get of me! Get off me!

(They gather up his clothes and carry them and the chair to the rear of the stage and stay there themselves).

(The Emperor, having now broken free of them, manages to push past Widow T).

M U S I C # 6 "Yakety Sax Music"

> Emperor runs out SR chased by Widow T.
> He reappears from SL followed by Widow T.
> He again runs out SR chased by Widow T.
> He reappears from SL, but Widow T. has doubled back from SR so they meet centre stage.

WIDOW T:   Come here you great big handsome hunk!

(She grabs him by his scarf and pulls him towards her, giving him a huge kiss on his cheek, hopefully leaving a large lipstick outline on the cheek facing the audience.)

EMPEROR:     Erg, urgh, yuck, 'orrible, 'orrible (etc.)

(he runs and jumps around, wiping his cheek in disgust and generally making a great big fuss........He suddenly stops, walks downstage, faces the audience and thinks for a minute).

EMPEROR:     (to audience) Coming to think of it, that was actually rather nice. I enjoyed that so much I wouldn't mind another one of those! Come here to me, you sexy wench!

WIDOW T:    Keep your hands off me!  You should be ashamed trying to take advantage of a sweet, young, innocent girl!


M U S I C # 7    "You're The One That I Want"

(should be danced in the sensuous manner of the film, copying all possible movements done by Olivia/John in 'Grease'  The more seriously performed, the funnier it will be)

EMPEROR:        I got chills, they're multiplying
                And I'm losing control,
                'Cause the power you're supplying,
                It's electrifying!

WIDOW T:        You better shape up, 'cause I need a man
                And my heart is set on you
                You better shape up, you better understand
                To my heart I must be true.

EVERYONE:       You're the one that she wants (the one that she wants)
                Oo-oo-oo, honey
                The one that she wants (the one that she wants)
                Oo-oo-oo, the one she needs (the one she needs)
                Oh, yes, indeed.

                You better shape up!

WIDOW T:        Why should I let you kiss me?  It's raining men lusting after me.  Look at that man over there (pointing to man in audience)  You can't wait to jump my body, can you dear?  That man over there (ponting to another man)  he's so eager he looks as though he's about to jump on the stage.  Calm down dear, you'll do yourself an injury!  That one over there (pointing to another man) is panting so much his tongue is hanging out!  Put your tongue back in dear, I wouldn't like to be you when your wife gets you home!

That's the trouble with being gorgeous. It's a terrible burden fighting off the men. I bet you have the same trouble, don't you dearie? (pointing to a woman in the audience)

Your singing's all very well, but you better declare your intentions, Eggbert En-Jie Jingping, a girl wants more than songs, she wants a ring on her finger. Am I right, or am I right, ladies?

Flowers might make us sneeze, pretty words won't pay the rent, sweeties won't keep us warm at night. What we want is a great big, fat, diamond ring. Am I right, or am I right, ladies? (cups hand to ear)

EVERYONE:    You're right!

M U S I C # 8    "Diamonds Are A Girl's Best Friend"

WIDOW T:    A kiss on the hand may be quite continental,
But diamonds are a girl's best friend.
A kiss may be grand but it won't pay the rental
On your humble flat, or help you at the automat!

EVERYONE:    Men grow cold as girls grow old
And we all lose our charms in the end,
But square cut or pear shaped
These rocks don't lose their shape
Diamonds are a girl's best friend!

Tiffany's, Cartier, Fortnums and Masons,
Talk to her Eggbert, Eggbert, give her diamond rings.
There may come a time when a lass needs a lawyer
But diamonds are a girl's best friend.

Diamonds
Diamonds
I don't mean rhinestones
But diamonds
Are a girl's best friend.

(With hand on hip and walking one foot directly in front of the other, as on a catwalk, Widow T. walks sexily off SR with the Emperor following her)

EMPEROR:    Give us a kiss, one more kiss, you know you want to.......etc.

(moving CS and standing from SR to SL Willie W., Columbine, Princess Jasmine, Aladdin. Jasmine is carrying a bag from either Waitrose, Sainsbury or Ocado. Colimbine is carrying a bag from either Lidl or Asda.)

(Aladdin bows to Jasmine. She extends her hand and he gallantly kisses it).

ALADDIN:     At your service beautiful Princess Jasmine, my name is Aladdin Twankey.

(Willie gives an awkward bow to columbine. She extends her hand, and not knowing what to do with it, rubs his hands together, rubs them on his trousers, and then grasps her hand in his and shakes it round and round vigorously, and bumps into her clumsily)

WILLIE W:     At your service beautiful handmaiden Columbine. My name is Willie Wonker... Wombey ... Wispey ... Washee.  Willie Washee.

JASMINE:     It's a pleasure to meet you Mr. Twankey.

COLUMBINE:  I'm glad we bumped into each other Mr. Washee.

JASMINE:     Seeing you Aladdin, I feel as though I've known you forever, or at least for a few days. Perhaps it's because two burglars have been breaking into the palace grounds. I caught sight of one of them, and do you know, by a remarkable coincidence, he looked exactly like you, Aladdin Twankey.

COLUMBINE:  I caught a glimpse of the other one, and do you know, by a remarkable coincidence, he looked  exactly like you, Willie Washee.

ALADDIN:     Have no fear beautiful princess, I am an expert at Kung Fu and I will protect you with my life!

(exhibits a couple of Kung Fu moves) (google 'Kung Fu Real Fighting Techniques')

W ILLIE W:     Have no fear beautiful handmaiden, I will be right behind him!

JASMINE:     When I awoke Monday morning, I found this lovely hairbrush under my bedroom window. (takes it out of the bag and holds it aloft.

COLUMBINE:  When I awoke Monday morning, I found this ugly toothbrush under my bedroom window. (takes it out of the bag and holds it aloft).

JASMINE:     When I awoke Tuesday morning, I found this scrumptious box of chocolates under my bedroom window. (changes hairbrush for chocolates and holds them aloft).

COLUMBINE: When I awoke Tuesday morning I found this rotting potato under my bedroom window. (changes toothbrush for potato and holds it aloft).

JASMINE: When I awoke Wednesday morning I found a beautiful red rose under my bedroom window. (changes box of chocolates for red rose and holds it aloft).

COLUMBINE: When I awoke Wednesday morning I found a mouldy carrot under my bedroom window. (changes potato for carrot and holds it aloft).

JASMINE: What do you think I will find under my bedroom window tomorrow, Aladdin?

ALADDIN : I think you will find my heart - no wait, you already have my heart Princess Jasmine.

JASMINE: I shall treasure it always.

COLUMBINE: What do you think I will find under my bedroom window tomorrow, Willie?

WILLIE W: I think you will find my bladder - no wait, you already have my bladder handmaiden Columbine - no wait, that doesn't sound right.

COLIMBINE: I shall treasure it always.

(Aladdin takes Jasmine's left hand, Willie takes Columbine's right hand)

M U S I C # 9 "You're The Top" (Parody)

ALADDIN: You're the Top, you're a hot fudge Sundae,
You're the Top, you're a cake on Monday.
You're a strawberry tart, you're the salt on fish,
You're a bacon butty, a Christmas pud,
You're quite a dish.

WILLIE W: You're the spinach that turns my teeth green,
You're the fattest pumpkin I've ever seen,
You're the chocolate turnip I eat with my fish,
You're a broccoli, brussel, and cabbage pie
You're quite a dish.

ALADDIN & You're the jam, you're the crust on my pies,
WILLIE: You're the sauce on the top of French fries,
I'm a worthless wreck, a total mess, a flop,
But if baby I'm the bottom, you're the top!

| JASMINE & COLUMBINE: | You're the top, you're a wobbly jelly,<br>You're the chocolates while I'm watching telly.<br>You're a sausage roll and you're battered fish<br>You're an apple tart, with jam and cream<br>You're quite a dish. |
|---|---|

| EVERYONE: | You're the ketchup on my cheese on toast and<br>You're the gravy on my Sunday roast and<br>I'm a worthless wreck, a total mess, a flop<br>But if baby I'm the bottom, you're the top! |
|---|---|

(The Emperor enters from SR, followed by Widow T., who retrieves her bread on the way )

EMPEROR: (indignantly and pointing at Aladdin with outstretched arm) Who is that man who dares lay a hand on my daughter, the Royal Princess Jasmine Juniper Jingping, the fairest in all the land of Peking in China and all the surrounding districts!

ALADDIN: I have come to tell you of my great love for your beautiful daughter and to formally ask for her hand in marriage.

EMPEROR: Never! You're a wastrel not fit to worship at her feet!

ALADDIN: I love the beautiful Princess Jasmine. Tell me what I must do to win the hand of your daughter?

EMPEROR: It is decreed by our ancient laws that the man who will marry my daughter must be a Prince of the Realm and be knighted by the golden sword, Excalibur.

ALADDIN: Where is the sword? I'll go and get it.

EMPEROR: The golden sword, Excalibur, is embedded deep inside a rock in The Cave of Brazzadin in the heart of the Arabian desert. Many a man has tried and failed to pull the golden sword from the rock.

ALADDIN: I shall rescue the sword and return to marry your daughter.

EMPEROR: Arrogant fool! You think you can do what no man has ever been able to do? Very well, let everybody here witness (pointing to Aladdin) I hereby banish Aladdin Twankey from the city of Peking in China and all the surrounding districts! You shall never return unless you carry with you the golden sword, Excalibur. That will never happen, because it is written in our ancient laws the only man who will be able to rescue the sword, Excalibur, must possess the fire of a dragon, the sting of a bee, the kindness of a teddy bear and the courage of a lion. Go, never darken my kingdom again!

WILLIE W: Wait for me, Aladdin, I will go with you. I will travel to the ends of the earth, and even to the heart of the Arabian desert. You can count on me, Aladdin, I am your most loyal friend and companion. I will always be right behind you! Oh …. there won't be any hairy spiders dropping on my head in the desert, will there? What about scorpions? They won't climb up my trouser legs and bite me, will they? I'm not keen on snakes hissing in my face and buzzards could soar above me with powerful beaks, ready to eat my flesh!

COLUMBINE: Oh Willie, I shall miss you so, but I will wait forever ….well at least until next Tuesday. (she kisses him on the cheek).

WILLIE W: She kissed me!

M U S I C # 10 "Till I Kissed Her"

Never felt like this until I kissed you
How did I exist until I kissed you.
Never had you on my mind,
Now you're there all the time
Never knew what I missed until I kissed you, uh-huh
I kissed you, oh yeah!

EVERYONE: Things have really changed since he kissed her uh huh,
His life's not the same now that he kissed her, oh yeah,
Mmm, she's got a way about her
Now he can't live without her
Never knew what he missed until he kissed her, uh, huh
He kissed her, oh yeah.

She doesn't realize what she does to him
And he didn't realize what a kiss could be.
Mmm, she's got a way about her
Now he can't live without her
Never knew what he missed until he kissed her, uh-huh
He kissed her!

WILLIE W: She kissed me!

EMPEROR : Go !

WIDOW T: Here, Laddykins, take this loaf of bread for your dinner - you know you get cranky when you've got an empty tummy. (he tucks the bread in his shirt or pocket). Give mummy a kiss goodbye (holding his head between her two hands, she kisses him violently on each cheek – Aladdin has to endure). Keep well wrapped up so you don't catch a cold, and be sure to keep your bowels regular.

(clap of thunder and/or cymbals, light flashes/lights go out for a few seconds)

BRAZZADIN:    FREEZE!

(everybody, startled, turns away from the audience).

GOOSEBUMPS AND GOOSEBERRIES! (to audience) Did you hear what I heard boys and girls? Only a man with the fire of a dragon, the sting of a bee, the kindness of a teddy bear and the courage of a lion...... That's me! I shall be the man to free the golden sword Excalibur from where it is embedded deep inside a rock in the Cave of Brazzadin in the heart of the Arabian desert, then I will marry the beautiful Princess Jasmine, just see if I don't!

(he strides off and everybody comes to life in the usual manner)

EVERYBODY:    (everybody gives a sob or two and waves goodbye) Goodbye, Aladdin, goodbye!

COLUMBINE:    Goodbye, Willie, goodbye!

(they both exit SL, Willie W. behind Aladdin, more hesitantly, and with much trepidation).

WIDOW T:    Oh, my poor Laddykins, banished for ever! (sobs loudly!) I shall never see him again! You're a nasty old man, and to think I let you give me a cuddle in the back of the laundry! You will never have the pleasure of me again! Hit the road, Eggbert!

(laundry workers bring the piles of his clothes and thrust them at the Emperor)

M U S I C # 11  "Hit The Road Jack"

WIDOW T:    Hit the road, Eggbert and don't you come back no more,
No more, no more, no more.
Hit the road, Eggbert
And don't you come back no more!

EMPEROR:    Woah woman, oh woman don't treat me so mean
You're the meanest old woman that I've ever seen
I guess if you said so
I'd have to pack my things and go.

EVERYONE:    That's right!

EMPEROR:    What you say?

-23-

EVERYONE:     Hit the road, Eggbert and don't you come back no more,
              No more, no more, no more.
              Hit the road, Eggbert
              And don't you come back no more.

EMPEROR:      Now baby, listen baby, don't you treat me this way
              'Cause I'll be back on my feet one day.

EVERYONE:     Don't care if you do 'cause it's understood
              You ain't got no money, you just ain't no good.

EMPEROR:      Well, I guess if you say so
              I'd have to pack my things and go.

EVERYONE:     That's right!

EMPEROR:      What you say?

EVERYONE:     Hit the road, Eggbert and don't you come back no more
              No more, no more, no more.
              Hit the road, Eggbert
              And don't you come back no more.

(Emperor gathers up his clothes and moves offstage, SR)

              (as the curtain slowly closes..........)

EVERYONE:     Hit the road, Eggbert and don't you come back no more
              No more, no more, no more,
              Hit the road, Eggbert
              And don't you come back no more.

              Curtain closed

M U S I C # 12   "Scheherazade"

### A C T  1   S c e n e  2

Somewhere in the Arabian desert. An elderly tramp enters from SL wearing dirty, old, baggy trousers and jackets. He wears an old hat which he takes off for begging, and carries some kind of old carpet-bag. He walks slowly with a little difficulty and a slight limp.

Unscripted in the following two scenes, Willie W. should feel free to act the clown, showing fear or pleasure, be ready to take/give the magic lamp from Aladdin, generally ad lib "I'm right behind you, Aladdin", etc., but most importantly, be the person most able to encourage audience participation

During the following dialogue Aladdin several times attempts to pass by the tramp, but is always blocked.

TRAMP:    (holding out his hat) Hey mister, spare a little money for a poor hungry guy?

ALADDIN:    (tries to get past) No, no, leave me alone.

TRAMP:    Come on, pal, help a poor tramp down on his luck, I'm really hungry, haven't eaten all day (holding out his hat) Come on mister, spare a few pennies.

ALADDIN:    (tries to get past) Don't bother me, I'm in a hurry.

TRAMP:    People who are hurrying to somewhere, are usually hurrying from somewhere. Where have you come from?

ALADDIN:    Peking, in China.

TRAMP:    Peking, eh?  That's where all the rich people live. Where do you work?

ALADDIN:    (tries to get past) In my mum's laundry.

TRAMP:    Your mum got her own business, eh? I hear there's a lot of money to be made in dirty underwear. Come on mister, spare a few pennies?

ALADDIN:    We can hardly make ends meet.

TRAMP:    I bet you have it easy, your mum owning a laundry, and her showering you with money.

ALADDIN:    (tries to get past) I spend all day washing and scrubbing and my mum doesn't even give me pocket money.

TRAMP: But you get plenty to eat, big slices of pizza with lashings of cheese on top; makes my mouth water thinking about it. Come on mister, spare a few pennies?

ALADDIN: (tries to get past) Oh, stop feeling sorry for yourself. I'm tired of people like you blaming everyone else for your troubles. If you want to eat, get yourself a job.

TRAMP: Do you think I was always like this? I was once like you, young and full of hope for the future. I thought I was going to be young forever. I had a job, many jobs, but when the work is finished and you get old they throw you out, don't want anything more to do with you. (lets Aladdin past)

M U S I C # 13 "Brother Can You Spare A Dime?"

(as he begins to sing, Aladdin starts to walk a few steps past him, but stops with his back towards the tramp. Each time the tramps sings "brother, can you spare a dime?" Aladdin turns back towards the tramp, hesitates, but then turns away from him again).

(the song should be sung quickly, in a defiant manner so as not to slow the panto and to keep up the high energy).

Once I built a railroad, made it run
Made it race against time.
Once I built a railroad, now it's done.
Brother, can you spare a dime?

Once I built a tower to the sun
Bricks and mortar and lime.
Once I built a tower, now it's done.
Brother, can you spare a dime?

Once I built a freeway and trucks could run,
Tar and concrete and lines.
Once I built a freeway, now it's done.
Brother, can you spare a dime?

Once I built big houses facing the sun,
Gave them all a picket fence.
Once I built big houses, now they're done.
Brother, can you spare a dime?

(Aladdin now faces and comes back towards him)

ALADDIN: I'm sorry, I'm really sorry, I was a fool. I don't have any money, but I'd like to give you this loaf of bread (takes the loaf of bread from inside his shirt) I was saving it for my Sunday dinner, but here, you take it (hands him the bread) I'm really not very hungry.

TRAMP:    Thank you, young man, not many people would give their last loaf of bread to an old tramp. Tell me, where are you going?

ALADDIN:   I am trying to find The Cave of Brazzadin.

TRAMP:    That's a bad, bad, place you're going to. I hear you have to pass through a ravine guarded by ferocious animals who could tear you to pieces. Even if you were to reach the cave, it is haunted by ghosts and ghoulies and other strange and weird things that come out in the dark. Sometimes at night, when the wind is in the east you can hear them from miles away chanting their horrible spells. Why would you want to go to such a terrible place?

ALADDIN:    I am in love with the beautiful Princess Jasmine, but her father, the Emperor, will not let me marry her unless I bring him the golden sword, Excalibur.

TRAMP:    Many a man has tried and failed to rescue Excalibur. Only one man is destined for success. He must have the fire of a dragon, the sting of a bee, the kindness of a teddy Bear and the courage of a lion. Are you determined to reach the cave and rescue the sword?

ALADDIN:    I am.

TRAMP:    Very well. Because you gave me, an old tramp, your last loaf of bread, I will return your kindness by giving you something very special. (he takes the lamp from his carpet bag and gives it to Aladdin). It is an old lamp. It may not look like much, but it is a magical lamp and contains great powers. It will help you on your difficult journey.

        Goodbye, young man, good luck to you.l

ALADDIN:    Thank you, I will always remember you and treasure the lamp forever.

(the tramp exits SR. Aladdin looks until he is out of sight and sighs in a tired manner).

(to audience) I am so tired. Sometimes I feel like giving up, but then I remember my love for Princess Jasmine and that keeps me going on, no matter how weary I am.

(a clap of thunder and/or cymbals. 3 seconds of darkness, a flash of light).
(Aladdin, startles, turns away from the audience and 'freezes' as Brazzadin shouts...)

BRAZZADIN:    FREEZE!

PUMPKINS AND PORCUPINES! Aladdin is still trying to walk to the cave. I must never let him reach it! (to audience) watch me closely and you will see how I shall use my evil powers to stop him!

(with outstretched arm, he points his finger at Aladdin)

>Twiddle diddle dumpling,
>Diddle twiddle dee,
>I can see him, but he can't see me.
>When he walks forward
>I'll make him walk back
>Watch where he goes
>When I shout ...... BACK!

(Aladdin 'moonwalks' towards SR until Brazzadin tells him)..... STOP!

GOOSEBERRIES AND GALOSHES!    What is Aladdin carrying?

(he walks to Aladdin and studies him from all sides).

Is it, could it be?  Yes, it is, it's the magic lamp! Aladdin is master of the  magic lamp!  If he should ever find out that if he rubs the lamp clean then out will fly the great Blue Genie, he will  triumph over me. That must never happen.

(to audience) If Aladdin asks you, " Shall I rub the lamp clean, or throw the lamp away?" You must tell him, "throw the lamp away!" Then The Great Blue Genie will never fly out of the lamp, and you don't want to see The Great Blue Genie, do you children?  Yes or no!? (cups hand to ear) I can't hear you children, shout louder, You don't want to  see The Great Blue Genie, do you children?  Yes or no!?

Don't tell me "yes" I, Brazzadin,  the evil magician, will tell you children what you want! I shall go now, but I will return to cast my evil spells on Aladdin, so that very soon I will be the one to marry the beautiful Princess Jasmine.

(Brazzadin exits and Aladdin, first a little dazed, starts to recover).

ALADDIN:    I don't see what's magic about this lamp, it's just a dirty old lamp that will need lots of rubbing to get it clean.  Maybe I should just throw the lamp away.  What do you think, children, shall I rub the lamp clean, or throw the lamp away? (cups hand to ear) I'm sorry, children, I can't hear you.  Shout louder!  Shall I rub the lamp clean, or throw the lamp away?

Well ...... if you're really sure, I will rub the lamp clean.

(he rubs it vigorously with large, exaggerated strokes to be easily seen by the audience)

Silly lamp, nothing is happening, it's just as dirty as ever!

(he tries rubbing it vigorously again)

I'm getting so fed up and cross with this stupid lamp!

(he stamps his foot angrily and the with a long, exaggerated sweep of his arm gives the lamp a big slap! The light go out briefly/clash of cymbals, flash of blue light and The Blue Genie comes in from SL, stumbling and tripping over his feet and holding his bottom).

BLUE G:    OW! OW! OW! That hurts! That really hurts! (looks at Aladdin) You! It was you! You slapped my bottom!

ALADDIN:   I didn't, I mean, I didn't mean to, sir.

BLUE G:    What a strange boy! Do you have a driver's licence to operate my lamp?

           Allow me to introduce myself. I am the one and only, world famous, magnificent and, as you can see, remarkably good looking, Blue Genie!

ALADDIN:   This isn't one of those magic lamps where a Blue Genie can grant me wishes, is it?

BLUE G:    Well, that depends, what day of the week is it?

ALADDIN:    ........... day

BLUE G:    Then you're in luck. We've got a special on this year. Two for the price of one and a beef hamburger to go. (hands Aladdin a hamburger bun)

ALADDIN:   This beef hamburger doesn't have any beef in it.

BLUE G:    Of course not, it's a vegetarian beef hamburger.

ALADDIN:   But it doesn't have any lettuce and tomato in it either.

BLUE G:    (takes back the roll) Oh, I got a bit hungry when I first went into the lamp.

ALADDIN:   When was that?

BLUE G:    I Don't know. What time is it?

ALADDIN:    (looks at his watch and tells him the time).

BLUE G:    Then it must have been one thousand, six hundred and eighty-seven years ago. Time does fly when you've having fun, doesn't it? I suppose now you've made me miss East Enders, you'll be sending me back into the lamp again, and my back gets all achy sitting in there cramped up. Give us a massage, would you?

(Blue G. will have to hold the lamp and return it after the massage. As Aladdin gives the back and neck massage, Blue G.wriggles with pleasure)

Ooooh, that's lovely, just there, down a bit, to the left, no, up a bit, you've missed a bit.

ALADDIN:    (stops) Does that feel better?

BLUE G:    Best you can do, I suppose. All this jumping in and out of the lamp every time someone wants a wish is getting a bit much at my age. Sometimes I think I'd like to break free. I do have other things I could be doing with my time you know.

M U S I C # 1 4   "I Want To Break Free"(Parody)

(he sings to audience, wildly enthusiastically, waving his arms around in pure comical drama)


I want to break free,
I want to break free,
I want to break free with my heart
I'd like to swim with the sharks teach goldfish
To bark and that's why
I know, I know I wanna break free!

Teach an ostrich to
Swim, take my cat to the gym
Ride a camel with humps and a
Big donkey that jumps, 'cos
That's why I know, I wanna break free!

I want to break free,
I want to break free,
I'd teach pigs how to fly right up
To the sky and lizards will smile 'cos
We dance with great style,
That's why I know, I wanna break free!!!

(he bows deeply several times to each side of the audience)

Thank you, thank you, thank you!  Available for weddings, birthdays and 'Britain's Got Talent.' £60 per hour, double on Sunday, plus all the cake and ice cream I can eat, don't forget the chocolate sprinkles.

What year is it?

ALADDIN:    Two thousand and ............

BLUE G:     Thought so, time for my yearly bath. Gotta be going. See ya!

ALADDIN:   Hey, what about my wishes?!

BLUE G:     Yeah, yeah, later, later. (he exits SR)

ALADDIN:    Well, that was one weird Genie!

(during the following, two very jolly policemen enter from SL chatting happily to each other).

ALADDIN:     (to audience) I wish I knew where I could find the Cave of Brazzadin. It's a shame there are no policemen in the desert, I could ask them for directions.

LEN/HEN:     (pointing their fingers at Aladdin) You're under arrest!

(Lenny and Hendy, the two policemen, laugh uproariously at their own jokes and give each other 'high fives' bump hips, run in little circles around each other, etc)

ALADDIN:     What for?

LENNY:      For wearing   (whatever colour he is wearing) pantaloons on a Sunday.

ALADDIN:    But today is   ............. day.

HENDY:      Then we're arresting you for not wearing purple pants on a ............ day! (laughter, 'high fives')

LENNY:      I think we should arrest him for exceeding the speed limit.

HENDY:      Ok, we're arresting you for walking 65 miles an hour in a 15 miles an hour speed zone.

ALADDIN:    But I can't walk more than 5 miles an hour.

LENNY:      Then we'll arrest you for walking 5 miles per hour in a 10 miles an hour speed zone!  (laughter, they bump hips)

HENDY:      I think we'd better follow you to the police station.

ALADDIN:    Why?

LENNY:      Because we can't remember the way! (laughter, they run in little circles round each other)

ALADDIN:    Where are you from?

HENDY:        ................ (local town)

ALADDIN:     What part of  ................ (local town)

LEN/HEN:     All our parts!  (laughter - bump hips)

LENNY:        (Taking notebook & pencil from pocket) We'll have to take your particulars.

ALADDIN:     I don't want to give you my particulars.

HENDY:        Why, aren't you wearing any?!

LENNY:        You'll need  to answer the following question:

HENDY:        What did the policeman say to his tummy?

ALADDIN:     I don't know, what did the policeman say to his tummy?

LEN/HEN:     You're under A VEST!  (laughter, they bend double, slapping their knees)

LENNY:        What do you call a flying policeman?

ALADDIN:     I don't know.  What do you call a flying policeman?

LEN/HEN:      A HELICOPPER!   (laughter, Hendy slaps Lenny on the back)

HENDY:        What did the policeman's left eye say to his right eye?

LEN/HEN:       Between you and me, (pointing to their noses)  SOMETHING SMELLS!
(laughter, they link arms and run around each other in little circles)

M  U  S  I  C  #  15   "The Laughing Policeman"

( at each chorus of laughter they link one of their arms in each side of Aladdin and go
around  anti clockwise in large circles. They stop when they start to sing again).

(at next chorus of laughter they turn around, link their opposite arms in each side of
Aladdin, making him go backwards as they go clockwise in large circles.

The chorus is:      Ha, ha, ha, ha, ha, ha, ha,
                            Ha, ha, ha, ha, ha, ha, ha,
                            Ha, ha, ha, ha, ha, ha, ha,
                            Ha,  ha, ha, ha, ha, ha, ha!

(Len/Hen are either side of Aladdin with arms linked with his, facing audience)
(Aladdin looks at one and the other very puzzled, until he joins in the 2<sup>nd</sup> verse)

LENNY/
HENDY:

I know a fat old policeman, he's
    Always on our street.
A fat and jolly red faced man, he
    Really is a treat.
He's too kind for a policeman, he's
    Never known to frown,
But everyone says he is, the
    Happiest man in town!

(chorus of laughter, with arms still linked, circling anti clockwise)

EVERYONE:
(facing
Audience)

He laughs upon point duty, he
    He laughs upon his beat,
He laughs at everybody when he's
    Walking down the street.
He never can stop laughing
    He says he never tried
But once he did arrest a man
    And laughed until he cried!

(chorus of laughter, with opposite arms linked, circling clockwise, Aladdin going backwards)

(facing
Audience)

So if you chance to meet him
    When walking round the town
Just shake him by his fat old hand
    And give him half a pound.
His eyes will beam and sparkle
    He'll gurgle with delight
And then you'll start him laughing
    With all his blessed might!

(chorus of laughter, with opposite arms linked, circling anti clockwise, towards the end of chorus, the policemen leave Aladdin standing CS, as they exit SR still laughing)

ALADDIN:    (to audience) Well, they weren't much help. I must walk on and try to find The Cave Of Brazzadin.

(a clap of thunder and/or cymbals, 3 seconds of darkness, a flash of light)
(Aladdin, startles, turns away from the audience and 'freezes' as Brazzadin shouts....)

BRAZZADIN:    FREEZE!

BAKED BEANS AND BEANSPROUTS! Aladdin is still trying to walk to the Cave Of Brazzadin! Watch how I shall use my evil powers to stop him! (points finger at Aladdin)

> Scooby dooby dooby,
> Dooby Scooby doo.
> Wherever he goes, I'm going too.
> When he walks forward
> I'll make him walk back.
> Watch where he goes
> When I shout "BACK!"

(Aladdin, after turning slightly, 'moonwalks' towards SR until Brazzadin tells him ........)

STOP!    Now I, Brazzadin, the most powerful magician in the world, will cast my most evil spell to stop Aladdin reaching The Cave Of Brazzadin. If you listen very carefully, children, you will hear the big, ferocious animals I will send running down the mountain to attack Aladdin. Watch how he will run away in terror!

> Jiggle Giggle Tiggle
> Tiggle Giggle Gee,
> Hear the animals roar
> But they won't bite me!

(he stalks out SL. Aladdin, dazed, stumbles a little, but starts to recover)

ALADDIN:    I'm so tired. I feel I've been walking for miles, but never seem to get anywhere ,

(there is a loud 'dragon' roar! This can be done by whatever means is at your disposal, even If necessary from voices backstage. A large 'dragon tail' could appear from side or backstage - if a large 'dragon tail' is available!)

ALADDIN:   What was that roar?

(an even louder 'dragon' roar!)

Could it be the big, ferocious animals that guard The Cave Of Brazzadin?

(an even louder 'dragon' roar!)

I wonder if the Blue Genie could help me?  What do you think, children, should I rub the magic lamp to make the Blue Genie appear?  Yes or no? (cups hand to ear) I'm sorry, children, I can't hear you.  You will have to shout louder.  Yes or No! (cups hand to ear) Ok, I will rub the magic lamp and see if I can make the Blue Genie appear.

(Aladdin rubs the lamp vigorously - nothing happens)

ALADDIN:     Phew, it's really hard to get the Blue Genie to come out of this lamp

(he tries again, even more vigorously. A clash of cymbals, 2 seconds of darkness, a flash of blue light, and the Blue Genie comes tumbling onto the stage from SL)

BLUE G:     Do you have to be so rough! You knocked me off the sofa as I was having my afternoon nap! I suppose you want some more wishes!

ALADDIN:     I haven't had any wishes yet!

BLUE G:     Don't argue. What do you want now?

ALADDIN:     Just listen to those dragons roaring!

(a loud 'dragon' roaring sound)

BLUE G:     Whooeee! That's so scary my hair's standing up on end! I'm getting out of here fast! Nice talking to you, see ya, I'm gone!

(he makes a run past Aladdin to SR, but as he goes past, Aladdin grabs him by the arm and pulls him back)

ALADDIN:     Not so fast! You're the Blue Genie, I'm your master, and I want a wish now!

BLUE G:     Oh, alright, stop complaining and hurry up, I don't want any dragons storming down the mountains blowing fire and smoke at me and messing up my ensemble. What do you think of it, a Dior design darling and the underpants are by Gucci? Hey, wanna see my underpants?

(he attempts to pull his trousers down to show him)

ALADDIN:     No, no, I don't want to see your underpants!

BLUE G:     You're such a spoilsport. Oh well, get on with it then, wish away!

ALADDIN:     I wish ...... I wish ...... (he hesitates, thinks, then...... ) I know, I wish for a weapon to fight the fiery dragons!

BLUE G:     Here goes then!

(he stands facing the audience and straining as though desperately trying to give birth, frantically working his elbows up and down)

WHOOSH! WHOOSH! WHOOSH!

It's no good, I just can't do it by myself, I need your help. Will you all WHOOSH with me? I'll say READY! STEADY! And then we'll all go WHOOSH! WHOOSH! WHOOSH! together, Ok? (frantically working his elbows up and down) READY! STEADY!

EVERYBODY:   WHOOSH! WHOOSH! WHOOSH!

BLUE G:      It's coming, I can feel the wish coming! Let's try again. (frantically working his elbows up and down) READY! STEADY!

EVERYBODY:   WHOOSH! WHOOSH! WHOOSH!

BLUE G:      That's it, I can feel the wish is almost here! Three more WHOOSHES will do it! (frantically working his elbows up and down) READY! STEADY!

EVERYBODY:   WHOOSH! WHOOSH! WHOOSH!

(thunder and/or cymbals, lights go out for two seconds, flash of blue light.....a water spray bottle comes sliding out from SR or Blue G takes it out from his shirt).

ALADDIN:     (picks it up, or takes it)  A water spray bottle! What type of weapon is a water spray bottle against fearsome dragons?!

BLUE G:      (to audience)  Whoops, guess I made a little boo-boo! Oh well, see ya!

(he exits hastily SR)

ALADDIN:     (runs after him a few steps towards SR) Come back here! Blue Genie, I command you to come back here!

BLUE G:      (from off stage) Gotta go, time for my pedicure!

(another loudest fearsome 'dragon' roar!)

ALADDIN:     Ok ferocious dragons, I'm ready for you!

('sexy' female dragon comes in from SL. She has a 'blow out.' Some, at least, of her (preferably) coloured hair could be showing. They meet roughly CS and begin circling each other like boxers. She will 'blow' at Aladdin and Aladdin will squirt the water spray bottle at her, being careful not to squirt too much and overly wet stage or her costume. They continue for a few moments and then she suddenly stops).

PUFFLEY:    Would you please stop squirting that thing at me, you're getting me all wet! Can't you see I've just had my hair done?!  What do you think of the colour?  (she pats her hair provocatively) I really fancied orange myself, but red (?) goes so well with my scales don't you think?

My scales do look gorgeous, don't they? (a little stroke of her scales)  It's the new body lotion I've been using. Brings up my shine something lovely. You could do with a bit of a shine yourself, your scales are looking quite drab and dry. (blows her blow out at him).

ALADDIN:   I must say I'm surprised, I thought dragons were supposed to blow fire and smoke.

PUFFLEY:    Smoke! Smoke! Are you crazy?!  Don't you know smoking's bad for you?! (Blows her blow out at him)

(Aladdin squirts the water spray at her and they begin circling each other briefly).

Waaah! (she begins to sob noisily)  Now look what you've done - squirted my nose and made all my make-up go streaky!  You're a big meanie!)

M U S I C # 16    "Fire Down Below"   (part parody)

        I'm getting mad 'cos you watered me,
        I'll blow smoke in your eyes so that you can't see,
        Keeping the temperature so high, I am a dragon so smart
        For there's a fire down below, down below in my heart.

        You'll be sorry you made a sweet dragon cry,
        Don't you yell at me, don't you dare to try.
        If you have anything in mind, warn you before you start,
        There is a fire down below, down below in my heart.

I sing beautifully, don't I?  Must be all that karaoke practice with Pavarotti.

What do you get when you cross a giraffe with a hedgehog?

ALADDIN:    I don't know, what do you get when you cross a giraffe with a hedgehog?

PUFFLEY:    A v...e...ry long toothbrush! (laughs hilariously at her own joke)  You'd better give me that ridiculous weapon before you do yourself an injury.

(she takes the spray bottle from Aladdin, puts it somewhere convenient, or carries it)

(there is a buzzing sound offstage. This can be done by whatever means available, or if necessary by voices offstage........Buzzz  Buzzz  Buzz!)

ALADDIN:   Do you hear that strange noise?

(a louder Bzzz Bzzz Bzzz!)

PUFFLEY:   You're in big trouble! Sounds like the bees who guard the Cave of Brazzadin. I think the bees are getting ready to swarm down the mountain, stinging everyone in their path.  Oooh, I wouldn't want to be in your shoes when they catch you!

(an even louder Bzzz Bzzz Bzzz!)

I wonder if the Blue Genie could help me  What do you think, children, should I rub the magic lamp and see if I can make the Blue Genie appear? Yes or no?  (cups hand to ear) I'm sorry children, I can't hear you. You will have to shout louder. Yes or No!  (cups hand to ear)  Ok, I will rub the magic lamp and see if I can make the Genie appear.

(he rubs the lamp vigorously, nothing happens)

It's really hard to get the Blue Genie to come out of this magic lamp. I'll try again.

(he tries again, even more vigorously.  A clash of cymbals, 2 seconds of darkness, a flash of blue light and Blue Genie tumbles on to the stage from SL).

BLUE G:   Do you have to be so rough! You knocked me clean off my step ladder just as I was about to change a light bulb! I suppose you want another wish. What now?!

ALADDIN:   Well, just listen to those bees buzzing!

(the loudest Bzzz Bzz Bzzz!)

BLUE G:   Whooeee! That's so scary my hair's standing up on end! I'm getting out of here fast!  Nice talking to you, see ya, I'm gone!

(he makes a run past Aladdin to SR, but as he goes past, Aladdin grabs him by the arm and pulls him back)

ALADDIN:   Not so fast! You're the Blue Genie, I'm your master, and I want a wish now!

BLUE G:   Oh alright, stop complaining and hurry up! I don't want any bees storming down the mountain and biting me on my bottom. (pats his bottom) What do you think of my trousers?  Got them at the car boot sale. Wanna try them on?

(attempts to take off his trousers)

ALADDIN:   No, no, I don't want to try on your trousers!

BLUE  G:      You're such a spoilsport.  Oh well, get on with it then, wish away!

ALADDIN:      I wish.....I wish  (he hesitates, thinks, then.....)  I know, I wish for a weapon to fight the buzzing bees.

BLUE  G:      Here goes then!

(he stands facing the audience and straining as though desperately trying to give birth, frantically working his elbows up and down)

WHOOSH!  WHOOSH!  WHOOSH!

It's no good, I just can't do it by myself.  I need your help.  Will you all WHOOSH with me?  I'll say READY!  STEADY!  And then we'll all go WHOOSH!  WHOOSH!  WHOOSH! together, Ok?  (frantically working his elbows up and down)  READY!  STEADY!

EVERYBODY:  WHOOSH!  WHOOSH!  WHOOSH!

BLUE  G:      It's coming, I can feel the wish coming!  Let's try again.  (frantically working his elbows up and down)  READY!  STEADY!

EVERYBODY:  WHOOSH!  WHOOSH!  WHOOSH!

BLUE  G:      That's it, I can feel the wish is almost here!  Three more WHOOSHES will do it!  (frantically working his elbows up and down)  READY!  STEADY!

EVERYBODY:  WHOOSH!  WHOOSH!  WHOOSH!

(clash of cymbals, lights go out for a couple of seconds, flash of blue light......a fly swatter Comes sliding out from SR or Blue Genie takes it out from his tunic)

ALADDIN:      (picks it up or takes it)  A fly swatter!  What type of weapon is a fly swatter against a swarm of bees?!

BLUE  G:      (to audience)  Whoops, I guess I made a little boo-boo!  Oh well, see ya!
(he exits hastily SR)

ALADDIN:      (runs after him a few steps towards SR)  Come back here!  Blue Genie, I command you to come back here!

BLUE  G:      (from offstage)  Gotta go, time for my ballet lesson.

(loudest Bzzz!  Bzzz!  Bzzz!

ALADDIN:      (passes off the lamp to Puffley)  Ok stinging bees, I'm ready for you!

MUSIC # 17  "The Bee Song"

BIZZIE L:    Oh what a glorious thing to be
             A gorgeous looking busy-busy bee
             Whiling away the passing hours
             Pinching all the pollen from the cauliflowers.
             I like to be a busy-busy bee
             Being just as busy as a bee can be,
             Flying round the garden, brightest ever seen
             Taking back the honey to the dear old queen.

             Bzz-bzz-bzz-bzz, honey bee, honey bee,
             Bzz if you like, but you won't sting me.
             Bzz-bzz-bzz-bzz, honey bee, honey bee,
             Bzz if you like, but you won't sting me!

(as she is almost finishing the song, Aladdin leans back his arm in an attempt to try and give her one last almighty 'swat!'  However, at that moment she catches sight of Puffley, steps to the side, and Aladdin is propelled by the momentum to tumble across the stage towards SL. When he recovers, he walks back to where Puffley and Bizzie Lizzie are chatting not quite knowing what to do).

Like your nail varnish, Puffley, what's the colour, 'Caterpillar Lime?'

PUFFLEY:    No, it's 'Cabbage Green', was thinking about choosing 'Luscious Broccoli' but changed my mind. What do you think?

BIZZIE L:    Think you made the right choice. By the way, do you think my bum looks big in this? (turns to let Puffley see and wiggles a bit, slightly towards audience).

PUFFLEY:    No, you're looking good.

BIZZIE L:    Thanks, I've been working out at the gym lately. Did have a Personal Trainer, but I dropped a heavy weight on his big toe. What a carrying on, hopping around the room screaming in pain! I stung him on the bottom so he'd really have something to cry about!

PUFFLEY:    Men are so careless, aren't they?

BIZZIE L:    Who's this weird little guy, does he belong to you?

PUFFLEY:    Oh, that's just Aladdin. He's really quite nice, but not too smart. (gives a little giggle)  Ask him a riddle.

BIZZIE L:    Hey you, what flies in the air and goes zzub, zzub, zzub?

ALADDIN:   I don't know, what flies in the air and goes zzub, zzub, zubb?

BIZZIE L:   (to audience)  A bee flying backwards! (she and Puffley laugh hilariously at her joke)  (she takes the fly swatter from Aladdin)

(there is a roaring sound offstage) (google Grizzly Bear Roar YouTube, or it can be done by whatever means necessary, even  by voices off stage).

(a louder roar)

BIZZIE L:   Now you're in trouble, that sounds like the grizzly bears who guard the Cave of Brazzadin. They are about to come down the mountain ready to tear into pieces anyone who gets in their path. Ooooh, I wouldn't want to be in your shoes when they catch you!

(an even louder roar.   Aladdin takes the lamp from Puffley)

ALADDIN:   I wonder if the Blue Genie could help me? What do you think, children, should I rub the magic lamp and see if I can make the Blue Genie appear? Yes or no? (cups hand to ear) I'm sorry, children, I can't hear you. You will have to shout louder. Yes or No! (cups hand to ear) Ok, I will rub the magic lamp and see if I can make the Genie appear).

(he rubs the lamp vigorously, nothing happens)

(he tries again, even more vigorously)  A clash of cymbals, 2 seconds of darkness, a flash of blue light and Blue Genie comes tumbling onto the stage from SL very awkwardly with his legs bent outwards as though he were astride a horse)

BLUE G:   Do you have to be so rough! You knocked me right out of my Yoga Class! Have you any idea how hard it is to get out of the Lotus Position at my age? I suppose you want some more wishes.  What now?

ALADDIN:   Well, just listen to those grizzly bears roaring!

(the loudest roar)

BLUE G:   Whoooeee! That's so scary my hair's standing up on  end! I'm getting out of here fast! Nice talking to you, see ya, I'm gone!

(he makes a run past Aladdin to SR, but as he goes past, Aladdin grabs him by the arm and pulls him back).

ALADDIN:   Not so fast! You're the Blue Genie, I'm your master, and I want a wish now!

BLUE G:     Oh, alright, stop complaining and hurry up. I don't want bears storming down the mountain and tearing the clothes off me. They might leave me with nothing but my vest. Mind you, I'm wearing the prettiest pink vest that's got hardly any holes in it. Here, I'll let you try it on.

(he attempts to take off his shirt)

ALADDIN:    No, no, I don't want to try on your pretty pink vest!

BLUE G:     You're such a spoilsport. Oh well, get on with it then, wish away!

ALADDIN:    I wish.....I wish (he hesitates, thinks, then...) I know, I wish for a weapon to fight the grizzly bears.

BLUE G:      Here goes then!

(he stands facing the audience and straining as though desperately trying to give birth, frantically working his elbows up and down)

WHOOSH!  WHOOSH!  WHOOSH!

It's no good, I just can't do it by myself. I need your help. Will you all WHOOSH with me? I'll say READY! STEADY! And then we'll all go WHOOSH! WHOOSH! WHOOSH! together, Ok?

(frantically working his elbows up and down) READY! STEADY!

EVERYBODY:  WHOOSH!  WHOOSH!  WHOOSH!

BLUE G:      It's coming. I can feel the wish coming! Let's try again. (frantically working his elbows up and down)  READY! STEADY!

EVERYBODY:  WHOOSH!  WHOOSH!  WHOOSH!

BLUE G:      That's it, I can feel the wish is almost here! (Three more WHOOSHES will do it! (frantically working his elbows up and down) READY! STEADY!

EVERYBODY:  WHOOSH!  WHOOSH!  WHOOSH!

(thunder and/or cymbals, lights go out for two seconds, flash of blue light......a feather duster comes sliding out from SR or Blue G takes it out from his tunic)

ALADDIN:      (picks it up, or takes it) A feather duster! What type of weapon is a feather duster against a horde of grizzly bears. What am I supposed to do, tickle them?

BLUE G:     (to audience)  Whoops, I guess I made a little boo-boo! Oh well, see ya!

(he exits hastily SR)

ALADDIN:    (runs after him a few steps towards SR) Come back here! Blue Genie, I command you to come back here!

BLUE G:     Gotta go, time for my tap dancing class!

(Aladdin passes lamp to Bizzie L.)

ALADDIN:    Ok big ferocious grizzly bears, I'm ready for you!

(Teddy B. enters, growling. They meet and start to wrestle sumo style. G: Osaka 2019 Day 15 Hakuho v Kakuryu (minus falls!?) As they grapple, Teddy finds Aladdin an ineffectual opponent and as they are wrestling, he catches sight of Bizzy Lizzie, pushes Aladdin away. Aladdin goes tumbling away towards SL. When Aladdin eventually recovers, he goes behind Teddy, ineffectually hitting him with the feather duster, pummelling him, trying to jump on his back. Teddy doesn't even notice him as he is talking and singing)

TEDDY B.    Wow! Looking good, Bizzie Lizzie, you've filled out since I last saw you! Give Teddy a big bear hug! (holds out his arms for the big hug)

BIZZIE L:   You won't get any big bear hugs from me, you double crossing, cheating male. Last time I saw you, you were positively drooling, watching Honey Bee doing a song and dance striptease on top of the piano in the karaoke room.

TEDDY B:    Aw, Lizzie, you know I've never had eyes for anyone but you. Give Teddy a little sugar!

M U S I C # 18    "Sugar, Sugar"

> Sugar, ah honey, honey,
> You are my fav'rit bee
> And you've got me wanting you.
>
> I just can't believe the loveliness of loving you
> I just can't believe it's true.
> I just can't believe a bee like you is wanting me
> I just can't believe it's true.

At this point he becomes vaguely aware Aladdin is 'attacking' him. He casually turns to the right, and using his left arm, puts Aladdin in a neck lock, bending him nearly double. He continues to the right with Aladdin until he is again facing Bizzie. Aladdin sometimes makes a very ineffectual struggle by waving an arm or leg)

Sugar, ah honey, honey,
You are my fav'rit bee
And you've got me wanting you.
Ah honey, oh sugar, sugar
You are my fav'rit bee
And you've got me wanting you.

(looks down and notices Aladdin in the neck hold)

Who is this pesky little boy? Is he bothering you Bizzie? Just say the word and I will bang him on the head (makes a motion of banging Aladdin on the head with his right hand) (a moaning sound from Aladdin) or I will get hold of his head and screw it round and round until his head falls off. (makes a motion of screwing it round and round with his right hand) (an even louder moaning sound from Aladdin)

BIZZIE L:    Oh that's just Aladdin. He's really quite nice, but not too smart. (she gives a little giggle) Ask him a riddle, Teddy Bear.

TEDDY B:    Why shouldn't you take a bear to the zoo?

ALADDIN:    I don't know, why shouldn't you take a bear to the zoo?

TEDDY B:    (to audience)  Because he'd rather go to the movies! (they all laugh and/or groan at his joke)

(there is a roaring sound offstage. G: lions' roaring sounds.  Or this can be done by whatever means available, or if necessary by voices offstage)

ALADDIN:    listen, do you hear that strange noise?

(a louder roar.  Aladdin takes the lamp from Puffley

TEDDY B:    Now you're in trouble, that sounds like the lions who guard The Cave Of Brazzadin.  They're about to come down the mountain ready to rip into pieces anyone who gets in their path.   Ooooh, I want to be in your shoes when they catch you!

(an even louder roar)

I wonder if the Blue Genie could help me?  What do you think, children, should I rub the magic lamp and see if I can make the Blue Genie appear? Yes, or no? (cups hand to ear) I'm sorry, children, I can't hear you. You will have to shout louder. Yes or No!  (cups hand to ear) Ok, I will rub the magic lamp and see if I can make the Genie appear.

(he rubs the lamp vigorously, nothing happens)

It's really hard to get the blue Genie to come out of this magic lamp. I'll try again.

(he tries again, even more vigorously. A clash of cymbals, 2 seconds of darkness, a flash of blue light and Blue Genie tumbles on the stage from SL with arms outstretched to the side and running as far as (physically) possible with one foot directly in front of the other)

BLUE G:    Do you have to be so rough! You knocked me clean off my tightrope just as I was about to do a pirouette on one foot!   (He could demonstrate a pirouette if wished. G: The Next Step - How To Do A Pirouette)   I suppose you want some more wishes. What now?

ALADDIN:    Well, just listen to those lions roaring!

(the loudest roar)

BLUE G:    Whoeeee! That's so scary, my hair's standing up on end. I'm getting out of here fast! It's been nice talking to ya, I'm gone!

(he makes a run past Aladdin to SR, but as he goes past, Aladdin grabs him by the arm and pulls him back)

ALADDIN:    Not so fast, you're the Blue Genie and I'm your master, and I want a wish - now!

BLUE G:    Oh, alright, stop complaining and hurry up. I don't want lions roaring down the mountain and tearing the clothes off me. They might leave me with nothing but my socks. Mind you, I'm wearing some very pretty socks, yellow with purple dots, and I washed them last year, so they don't really smell that much. Here, I'll let you try them on.
(he attempts to take off his shoes)

ALADDIN:    No, no, I don't want to try on your smelly socks!

BLUE G:    You're such a spoilsport. Oh well, get on with it then, wish away!

ALADDIN:    I wish.....I wish (he hesitates, thinks, then.....) I know, I wish for a weapon to fight the roaring lions!)

BLUE G:    Here goes then!

(he stands facing the audience and straining as though desperately trying to give birth, he works his elbows up and down)

WHOOSH!  WHOOSH!  WHOOSH!

It's no good, I just can't do it by myself, I need your help. Will you all WHOOSH with me? I'll say READY! STEADY! And then we'll all go WHOOSH! WHOOSH! WHOOSH! together, ok? (frantically working his elbows up and down) READY! STEADY!

EVERYBODY: WHOOSH! WHOOSH! WHOOSH!

BLUE G:        It's coming, I can feel the wish coming! Let's try again. (frantically working his elbows up and down) READY! STEADY!

EVERYBODY:  WHOOSH! WHOOSH! WHOOSH!

BLUE G:        That's it, I can feel the wish is almost here!  Three more WHOOSHES will do it! (frantically working his elbows up and down) READY! STEADY!

EVERYBODY:  WHOOSH! WHOOSH! WHOOSH!

(thunder and or cymbals, lights go out for two seconds, flash of blue light ....... a pair of pliers come sliding out from SR or Blue Genie takes them out from his tunic)

ALADDIN:        (picks them up or takes them)  A pair of pliers! What type of weapon is a pair of pliers against a horde of roaring lions? What am I supposed to do, pull out their toenails?

BLUE G:        (to audience) Whoops, I guess I made a little boo-boo, oh well, see ya! (he exits hastily to SR)

ALADDIN:        runs after him a few steps towards SR) Come back here! Blue Genie I command you to come back here!

BLUE  G:        Gotta go, time for my line dancing class!

(another loudest roar. Aladdin could pass the lamp to Bizzie L.)

ALADDIN:        Ok big ferocious lions, I'm ready for you!

(Leopold the lion enters from SR. He must have a 'thorn' (stick) attached to or close to his right foot, perhaps by Velcro strip or an unobtrusive pocket sewn into his costume).

They both circle each other, Aladdin's arm outstretched to use the pliers to catch Leopold's claws, Leopold roaring and clawing the air, catlike. After a few moments it is seen Leopold is limping, and the limp quickly becomes worse, until he finally bursts into tears, rubbing his eyes and sniffing).

LEOPOLD:        You are such a meanie, attacking a poor little injured lion. Ow! Ow! My big toe really hurts! He hops around in pain blubbering.

ALADDIN:    There, there, don't cry. (he takes out the large handkerchief he has been carrying in his tunic) Here, blow your nose. (he blows the lion's nose, and then gives Leopold the handkerchief. Leopold then blows his own nose and then gives back the handkerchief for Aladdin to return to his tunic)

What's your name?

LEOPOLD:    Leopold (sniffing) and I've got a big thorn stuck in my foot, and it really hurts! (starts crying again)

ALADDIN:    I will help you. Give me your foot.

(ideally there will be something on stage where Aladdin can sit and Leopold could lift his foot on Aladdin's knee. If this is not possible, and the lion costume may make it difficult too, then Aladdin could just kneel in front of him)

(Aladdin should now make a great show of trying to pull out the 'thorn' while saying such things as " I've nearly got it" while Leopold is saying such things as "Ow, Ouch")

ALADDIN:    (triumphantly) There, I've got it out! (he displays the big 'thorn' aloft for the audience to see, then gives it to Leopold)

LEOPOLD:    Oh, thank you, thank you (he gives Aladdin an enormous 'bear hug' and 'kisses' him on both his cheeks) I shall now be your friend for ever, and ever. You can always trust me to be faithfully by your side for the rest of your life! Take a chance on me to always be your bestest friend.

M U S I C  #  19    "Take A Chance On Me"

(Leopold has his 'arm' around Aladdin's shoulders as he sings)

> If you need a friend, I'm the first in line
> 'Laddin I'm still free, take a chance on me
> If you need me, let me know, gonna be around
> If you've got no place to go, if you're feeling down.
>
> If you're all alone when your friends have flown
> 'Laddin I'm still free, take a chance on me
> Gonna do my very best and it ain't no lie
> If you put me to the test, if you let me try.
>
> Take a chance on me,
> Take a chance on me,
> Take a chance on ..........

(sees Puffley, forgets Aladdin, pushes him out of the way, and swaggers over to Puffley)

Who's this gorgeous creature with the sensuous tail? What say we go to my den and do a little tweeting together. You're not under age are you?

ALADDIN:     Hey, what about me?

LEOOLD:     I don't want to tweet with you. Who is this little guy anyway?

TEDDY:     Oh, that's just Aladdin. He's really quite nice, but not too smart. (gives a little giggle) Ask him a riddle, Leopold.

LEOPOLD:     What did the lion eat after the dentist pulled out his tooth?

ALADDIN:     Wait a minute, let me think. (turns to audience, thinks for a couple of seconds) I know what the lion ate after the dentist pulled his tooth. He ate .........the DENTIST!

EVERYBODY:   Hurrah, hurrah for Aladdin!

LEOPOLD:     Congratulations! And how can we help you, Aladdin?

ALADDIN:     I'm trying to find the Cave Of Brazzadin. I must rescue Excalibur, the golden sword.

LEOPOLD:     The Cave of Brazzadin? Why, it's just over there (points to SL exit) Look, you can see it from here.

ALADDIN:     (shielding his eyes with his hand) Where? Where is it?

(everybody points to SL exit)

I can see it! I can see it!

( Teddy B moves to Bizzie Lizzie and holds her hand. Leopold moves to Puffley and holds her hand, and they all wave goodbye with their free hands)

ALADDIN:     (as he turns and waves goodbye) Goodbye, Goodbye!

(they all call out 'goodbye' ' good luck' etc., as the curtain closes.

Curtain Closed

M U S I C  #  20    "Ghost Cerise"


A C T  2    S c e n e  1

The scene is The Cave Of Brazzadin. Lighting should be dim to create an air of scary mystery, lightening as the scene progresses.

The golden sword, embedded in a 'rock' could be illuminated with a single, preferably yellow/gold spotlight.

The stage is empty when Aladdin enters, but the 'creatures' enter silently and partially surround him. They keep roughly in pairs where possible  i.e.,   Phineas F/Maudie M, Caleb C/Daphne D,    Stanley S/Priscilla P.

ALADDIN:    (comes downstage and speaks to audience)  So this is the Cave Of Brazzadin, it's really very scary and I'm trying hard to be brave. I just have this scary feeling I'm not alone, as though there are frightening creatures all around me. I can't see them and yet I know they are here.

(As he's speaking, he gradually backs up. The 'creatures' now completely surround him and walk around him in a circle as they sing......)

M U S I C  #  21    "Hernando's Hideaway"  (parody)

CREATURES:     I know a dark and spooky cave
                Where spiders crawl around and wave,
                And ghosts and ghoulies misbehave,
                It's called the Cave of Brazzadin!

                (towards audience) BOO!

                All you can see are silhouettes
                And rats and bats are kept as pets
                Where no one likes the smell and yet
                It's called The Cave Of Brazzadin!

                (towards audience)   BOO!

PHINEAS F:     Are you scared yet?

ALADDIN:       I'm not scared of you, I don't think you really want to frighten me.

CREATURES:  WE DO! WE DO! (they continue circling him while waving their arms and making all kinds of 'ghostly' sounds)   WHOOH!  AARGH!  OOOh!  AAAH!  BOO!

( as each 'creature' speaks they should break the circle and come downstage towards the audience just a little)

ALADDIN:    I wish you'd stop making those silly noises. You'll be scaring all the nice children who've come to see their pantomime.

DAPHNE D:     (sounding pleasantly bewildered) But we've got to scare children, it's our job as ghosts and ghoulies to scare children.

ALADDIN      Well, these children are not scared of you. Are you scared of these silly ghosties, children?  Yes or no? (cups hand to ear)

EVERYBODY:   NO!   (hopefully!)

PRISCILLA P :   (in a pleasant manner) I think the children said yes.  Are you scared of us, children?  Yes or no? (cups hand to ear)

EVERYBODY:   NO!   (hopefully!)

MAUDIE M:    Oh, the shame of it, I shall never be able to hold my head up in Tesco again!

CALEB C: What's the use of ghoulies who can't scare people!

ALADDIN:     ALADDIN: Well, you could start by being nice to the lovely boys and girls and mums and dads.

STANLEY S:   (coming to audience, waves, goes all shy and giggly) Hallo boys and girls and mums and dads)  (to Aladdin) Was that alright? It feels so weird being nice to people.

ALADDIN:     You did very well, now you can start being nice to each other. Caleb Carbuncle, is there anything nice you'd like to say to Daphne Dysentery? (Caleb C. all embarrassed and giggly shakes his head)   Stanley Stagnacious is there anything nice you'd like to say to Priscilla Pestilence? (Stanley S. All embarrassed and giggly shakes his head) Phineas Fungus, is there anything nice you'd like to say to Maudie Maggot?

PHINEAS F:   How can a plain old skeleton like me say anything to a beautiful mummy like Maudie Maggot?

ALADDIN:     Well, I think you should sing a love song to Maudie Maggot. (to audience) what do you think boys and girls and mums and dads, should Phineas Fungus sing a love song to Maudie Maggot? Yes or no? Cups hand to ear)

EVERYBODY:   Yes! (hopefully!)

(Phineas goes to Maudie M. and takes her hand, Caleb C. and Stanley S., very shyly shuffle to Daphne D. And Priscilla P. And take their hands.

M U S I C  #  22    "You Must Have Been A Beautiful Baby"

PHINEAS F:   You must have been a beautiful baby,
             You must have been a wonderful child
CALEB C      When you were only startin' to go to kindergartin'
             I bet you drove the little boys wild.
STANLEY S:   And you have got the cutest red dimples
             And they come with two sexy blue eyes.
PHINEAS F:   When I'm looking at those lips and you're swaying both those hips
             I tremble at the sight of you.
PH/CAL/STA:  You must have been a beautiful baby,
             'Cause baby, look at you now!

EVERYBODY:   Yes, you must have been a beautiful baby,
             'Cause baby, look at you now!

MAUDIE M:    Oh, thank you Aladdin, you have shown us it is much better to be nice to nice people.

DAPHNE:      I'm not sure I want to be nice to nasty people.

PRISCILLA    We'll be nice to all the nice people and nasty to all the nasty people!

PHINEAS F:   And now, Aladdin, it's time for you to rescue the golden sword.

(Aladdin advances towards the sword, with the creatures following him, hopefully leaving space at the SL area)

(clap of thunder and/or cymbals, light flashes/lights go out for a few seconds)

BRAZZADIN:   FREEZE! (everybody, startled, turn away from the audience)

BACK! BACK! I TELL YOU!

(Aladdin and the creatures 'moonwalk' towards SL, some moving there in a zig zag or semi circular route, especially if they are anxious to show off their 'moonwalking' skills and would otherwise get to SL too quickly!)

BEAN PODS AND BRUSSEL SPROUTS! (to audience) Aladdin has reached the cave, but he will not rescue the gold sword. Listen while I caste my evil spell!

OOGLEYBOOGLEY, BOOGLEYBOO!
He got to the Cave, but I did too.
I'll rescue Excalibur, the golden sword.
I'll pull from the rock I'll give you my word.
Aladdin is banished from the Kingdom
And I will marry the Princess Jasmine.
Once we are married she'll do as I say,
I will command and she will obey!

(Aladdin remains frozen, but the 'creatures' come to life and start to gradually position themselves between the sword and Brazzadin )

CALEB C:       (to audience) We have promised Aladdin we will be nice to nice people

STANLEY:       (to audience) But we will be nasty to nasty people.

PHINEAS F:     (to audience) Please tell us if Brazzadin is nice or nasty (cups hand to ear)

EVERYBODY:   He's nasty! (hopefully!)

PHINEAS F:     I'm sorry, I can't hear you, is the evil magician, Brazzadin, nice or nasty?

EVERYBODY:   He's nasty! (hopefully!)

MAUDIE M:    They say he is nasty!

DAPHNE D:    I think we should scare him!

PRISCILLA P:   Ok, let's scare him!

(They face Brazzadin, positioning themselves roughly between the sword and Brazzadin so he can't get to it. As they sing, they rock backwards and forwards, pointing at Brazzadin as they rock)

CREATURES :    We will, we will rock you,
                  We will, we will rock you.

               You got dirty old fingernails and big grubby toes
               And what you smell of nobody knows!
               You got mud on your face you big disgrace,
               Stomping around all over the place!

               We will, we will rock you,
               We will, we will rock you.

               Your hair has fleas and plenty of lice
               A hot soapy shower would really be nice!
               You got mud on your face you big disgrace,
               Stomping around all over the place!

               We will, we will rock you,
               We will, we will rock you.

BRAZZADIN:    Out of my way, out of my way. At last, Excalibur, the golden sword will be
Mine!

(he pushes them aside and they scatter around the sword)

(he stands before the sword, 'spits' on both hands, rubs them together, grasps the sword
and desperately 'pulls' it. He is unable to move it. He stops, walks all around it with
puzzlement and then struggles again to no avail.

POTATOES AND PORCUPINES!! It won't come out! I know, (to audience) Listen to this one,
my most evil spell!

               Hairy spiders, slithery snakes,
               Better join with the bats
               To play patter cakes.

               Wiggling worms and toads who fiddle
               Come here to me and watch frogs who giggle.
               Free the sword and it will be mine,
               Give it me NOW! I can't waste time!

(to audience)  watch me pull the sword from the rock!

(he 'spits' on his hands again, rubs them together and midst grunts and groans, tries again)

RADISHES AND RECYCLING BINS! It's useless, I can't do it! Who cares, I never wanted the stupid sword anyway!

(he stamps up and down with both feet, batters both fists against an unseen wall like a child having a tantrum, and then exits SL in a temper)

STANLEY S: Hurray, hurray, he's gone! (as Aladdin wakes up)

CALEB C: Are you ready to rescue the golden sword Aladdin?

PHINEAS F: Remember, the only person able to rescue the golden sword must have the fire of a dragon, the sting of a bee, the kindness of a teddy bear and the courage of a lion.

(they gather around the sword, leaving room so the audience has a clear view of Aladdin as he attempts to pull out the sword. Aladdin tentatively walks around it, and then stands in front of the handle)

MAUDIE M: Are you ready?

DAPHNE D: Are you steady?

PRISCILLA P: GO!

(Aladdin takes hold of the sword with both hands. There is a little resistance as he pulls, but then the sword suddenly comes free and with a cry of triumph Aladdin holds it aloft with both hands)

CREATURES: Hurray, Aladdin has rescued Excalibur, the golden sword!

(thunder clap and/or cymbals, light flashes/lights go out for a few seconds and Brazzadin enters from SL)

BRAZZADIN: FREEZE! (everybody freezes) Back, Back, I tell you! (everybody except Aladdin, still holding the sword aloft, 'moonwalks' back towards SR, being careful to leave SR entrance clear)

MAGGOTS AND MEERKATS! (to audience) You think Aladdin has got the sword but that was all part of my evil plan. I let Aladdin rescue the sword so I can steal it from him. That's why they call me The World's Most Evil Magician, Brazzadin!

(as he attempts to steal the sword, the 'creatures' start to come to life, but stay more or less in position, leaving SR entrance clear, miming fear, consternation etc.)

(Aladdin also comes to life, and still holding the sword aloft, he and Brazzadin grapple for the sword. Finally, Brazzadin wrests the sword from Aladdin's hands and with a great cry of triumph holds the sword above Aladdin as though to strike him on his head!)

(Aladdin frantically bends away from him, desperately trying to shield his face with his hands)

BRAZZADIN:    I got the sword, I got the sword, and you haven't!

(a clap of thunder/a flash of (red?) light. Brazzadin stands rigid with fear, the golden sword still held high above his head with both hands)

WIDOW T:    (from offstage)   BRAZZADIN!

BRAZZADIN:    (shouts in terror)   MUMMY!!

WIDOW T/J    (entering from SR) Brazzadin Twankey - what are you doing to your little baby brother?!

BRAZZADIN:    (sniffling or a few sobs)   Nothing, mummy.

ALADDIN:    He's picking on me!

BRAZZADIN:    He started it!

ALADDIN:    He's trying to steal my golden sword!

BRAZZADIN:    I got it first!

WIDOW T/J:    Stop picking on your little brother and give him his silly sword.
(Brazzadin gives him the sword and starts to wail!)

Oh, stop sniffling and blow your nose.
(blows his nose loudly on his sleeve - blow 'raspberry' to simulate the blow)

And look at your grubby face.
(Takes out a very large, grubby, holey, rag from her pocket, (gives a big (pretend) spit on it and holding the back of his head with her left hand, rubs his face vigorously with her right hand)

WIDOW T/J:    (holds his nose with left hand, right hand with dirty cloth holding his lower jaw open)

Did you brush your teeth this morning? Disgraceful, must be 10 centimeters of green mould in there, and goodness know what those big hairy things are crawling around inside.

Did you finish your homework before you went out to play with your evil magic spells? You know your new daddy, the Emperor, won't let you have the keys to the royal car unless you bring your grades up to a D average.

I don't know what's to become of you, Brazzadin. You need a good woman to take you in hand.

(Scabies S enters unobtrusively SL)

What about that one over there? She doesn't look too decrepit as far as skeletons go. Hey, you, the old bony one that looks like a wizened turnip. Come over here and let me take a look at you.

(Scabies comes over to her and Widow T/J prods and pokes her, and opens her mouth with both hands, turns her head this way and that, inspecting her teeth as though she was a horse.

Hmmm, she looks a bit long in the tooth. How old are you?

SCABIES S:     I'll be two hundred and sixty-six and three quarters next Tuesday.

WIDOW T:     I suppose she's wearing quite well considering. She's certainly not much to look at, rather a scraggy thing, but at least she won't cost you much in food. What's your name?

SCABIES S:     Scabies Salmonella.

WIDOW T:     Brazzadin, come over here, I've got one for you. (Brazzadin goes all shy and giggly as he shuffles next to his mother). Don't just stand there, I can't waste all day, I've got dinner to cook. (she pulls a huge ring from her right hand, 'spits' on it and rubs it shiny with her dirty grey handkerchief) Give her this.

BRAZZADIN:     (takes the ring from his mother, going all shy and giggling again as he shuffles over to Scabies. Cast members could help him get down on one knee. If this would cause physical difficulty he can remain standing).     You wanna do it or not?

SCABIES S:     I don't know, a young, innocent girl like me can't be rushed. I've got to give it a lot of thought. (she snatches the ring from his hand, inspects it all over, gives it a big bite to test if the 'diamond' is real, puts the ring on her finger, waves it aloft for all to see.......)     Ok, I've thought, let's do it!

(cast members help Brazzadin to his feet and everyone claps enthusiastically)

MUSIC # 24        "Let's Do It"   (parody)

SCABIES S:          Birds do it, bees do it,
                    Even educated fleas do it
                    Let's do it, let's fall in love.

BRAZZADIN           Rats do it, bats do it
                    Even sophisticated cats do it,
                    Let's do it, let's fall in love.

EVERYBODY:          Moles do it, voles do it
                    Even hedgehogs creeping round at night do it,
                    Let's do it, let's fall in love.

WIDOW T/J:    That's enough singing, let's go home.

ALADDIN:      I can't go home, the Emperor has banished me from the kingdom.

WIDOW T/J:    Oh, don't take any notice of Eggbert, he's just so full of hot air he sometimes bursts like a balloon. Eggy, I tell him, you shouldn't get worked up, it isn't good for your blood pressure. Since I let him marry me (holds hand up to show a big ring to audience) and move us all into the Palace, he's become much better behaved. He's forgiven you and forgotten all about it - well, more or less! He's waiting outside.  Eggbert! Eggbert! Get in here and be nice to Aladdin!

(the Emperor reluctantly shuffles into the cave from SR, standing near to Widow T/J. Come here, Eggbert and make nice to Laddykins (pushes him towards Aladdin)

EMPEROR:      (mumbles loudly) Eegrh,  yrgh,  igh erch,  erg

(he turns tail, tries to run away towards SR, but she grabs hold of his belt, waistband, or whatever is available so that he is still working his elbows backwards and forwards and his legs are still running on the spot, but he isn't getting anywhere)

WIDOW T/J     Tell Aladdin you're sorry you banished him from the kingdom and you want him to come home.

EMPEROR:      (grumpily) Eegrh, yrgh, igh, erch, erg (she gives him a big prod with her elbow)  Owch!  What she said.

WIDOW T/J:    Tel Aladdin he'll be the son you never had.

EMPEROR:      (wailing as though in pain)  WHAH!

WIDOW T/J     Eggbert!

ALADDIN:     Oh, daddy (stretches out both his arms) Daddy, shall we hug?!

EMPEROR:     (wailing as though in pain) WHAH!

WIDOW T/J:  (too audience) Maybe that's asking too much!  Just give him his silly sword and we can all go home.

(Aladdin gives him the sword which he accepts ungracefully, putting it against his shoulder rifle style)

ALADDIN:     Can I bring my friends?  (gesturing towards the 'creatures")

WIDOW T/J:  Why not, they'll make cheap bridesmaids.

(a little clash of cymbals and blue light)

BLUE G:     (stumbles in from) SR I don't suppose I can come home with you, (a little sob) You don't need me any more (a little sob) I shall be so lonely without you (little sob)

ALADDIN:     What do you think boys and girls, mums and dads, should we take the Blue Genie home with us?  Yes or no? (cups hand to ear)

EVERYBODY:  Yes!

I can't hear you, shout loudly, should we take the Blue Genie home with us? Yes or no?

EVERYBODY:  Yes!

ALADDIN:     Silly Blue Genie, of course we all want you to come home with us. What would I do without my best friend?

(Blue G, very shy, but so happy, jumps up and down in pleasure)


M U S I C 25 #   "Coming Home Tonight"


ALADDIN:     I've been stuck in motion
             Moving too fast
             Tryna catch a moment but it slips through my hands
             All I see are long days and dark nights
             I'm lost without her, but I'm on my way, so hold tight.

EVERYBODY:     He's coming home tonight
Meet him in the valley where the kids collide into the morning.
Oh, my gosh, his town is coming alive
He's coming home tonight, I know you're ready for the sparks to fly
into the morning
Oh, my gosh, his town is coming alive
'Cause he's coming home tonight,
'Cause he's coming home tonight.

Curtain closing

'Cause he's coming home tonight,
He's coming home tonight,
Yes, he's coming home tonight.

Curtain closed.

MUSIC # 26    "Beautiful Chinese Music/Chinese New Year Instrumental
              Traditional Chinese Music"


                    A C T  2    S c e n e  2

The music can continue while the Palace is being decorated for a traditional Chinese wedding which can be done by actors or stagehands wearing regular clothes while The Herald is speaking. (for set ideas google " Our Traditional Chinese Wedding - full version." ) This is the panto's 'glamour' scene and can be decorated as well as facilities allow. There should be a table near the rear of stage covered with a red/gold cloth. SR and rear of table should be two chairs for the Emperor & Widow T/J.

(As the Herald enters from SL the music quiets and stops as he starts to speak)

(Towards the end of The Herald's speech Aladdin will enter from SL with Blue Genie carrying a small bouquet of red flowers, Brazzadin, Willie Washee carrying a red envelope, Phineas F., Caleb C., Stanley S., with cut up pieces of newspaper to represent Chinese money, preferably hidden about their person).

HERALD:   (he will always address audience) Good evening boys and girls, ladies and gentlemen. We are gathered here today to witness the wedding between Sir Aladdin Abernathy Twankey and Princess Jasmine Juniper Jinping. I have been informed that we have with us here today some visitors from ………  ………  ……   …….. (name all local towns/villages etc., where the audience may have come from) who have travelled all the way from England to China to attend this Chinese Wedding Ceremony. Would those visitors please raise their hands?

Thank you, we are very pleased you have come and welcome you all. In honour of your visit, I will attempt to conduct the Ceremony in English and explain our ancient Chinese customs and rituals as we proceed.

Ancient Chinese tradition says the groom and his attendants must fetch the bride from her father's house and bring her to the wedding.

(Aladdin 'et al' start to bang at the 'door' at the SL entrance - big bangs, knocks, etc.) Let us in, we've come to escort the bride, let us in, etc. etc. (they go into a huddle, then go back to the Herald wondering what to do next)

ALADDIN:   What are we going to do?  I've got to escort Princess Jasmine to the wedding, but the bridesmaids won't let us in!

HERALD:   Ancient Chinese tradition says the groom must show the bride is such a prized possession he is willing to pay money in order to gain her hand in marriage.

(Columbine, Maudie M, Daphne D, Priscilla P enter from SR demanding money)

BRIDESMAIDS: Show us the money! Give us some money! We want money! Pay us money!

(Willie W. hastily runs around to the 'attendants' and they rummage around on their person and put wads of notes (preferably held together with possibly staples) into the red envelope, which Willie hurriedly hands around to the 'bridesmaids')

(A hasty counting, 1, 2, 3, etc.) Not enough money!  We want more money! Pay us more money!

(Willie W hurriedly collects more money from the 'attendants' and hands it to Columbine)

COLUMBINE:    If that's all you've got, I suppose it'll have to do. Bring the bridal bouquet!

Blue Genie hands the bouquet to Aladdin and they all exit SR.

HERALD:        Ladies and gentlemen, i have the great honour to present The Grand Emperor Eggbert En-Jie Jingping and his beatif ....... well, his wife, The Grand Empress Lady Letitia Twankey Jingping .

(Widow T/J enters backwards from SR dragging the Emperor by his rear waistband. He is reluctantly having to run backwards, waving his arms and saying "don' wanna, can't make me, lemme go" etc. She finally manages to get him to his seat and pushes him down by his shoulders)

WIDOW T/J :   (to audience) That was a lot easier than I thought it was going to be! (sits down next to him)

M U S I C # 27    "Chinese Music Instrumental - Chinese Festival

(ideally the procession will proceed from auditorium R. If facilities do not allow then the procession will be a simpler affair, actors entering from SL and going to their respective places. In that case ignore procession instructions) .

(from auditorium R enter Alladdin, Jasmine wearing a red veil and carrying the red bouquet, Willie carrying golden sword like a rifle, Columbine carrying a red stick, Blue Genie carrying the 'magic' lamp, Brazzadin and Scabies S. Bridesmaids: Maudi M, Daphne D and Priscilla P. Attendants: Phineas F, Caleb C, Stanley S, and Primrose carrying a tin bow)

(when they get halfway down centre aisle music should stop)

HERALD:       HALT! One moment please! Ancient Chinese custom dictates the groom must prove his physical strength by carrying the bride on his back to the Wedding Ceremony.

(Princess J. Places her hands on Aladdin's shoulders and 'assisted' by Columbine and Willie W, makes inept efforts to clamber and jump on Aladdin's back until Aladdin staggers and sinks to his knees 'under the weight')

ALADDIN:    She's too fat!

(gasps from everyone!)

HERALD:    I wouldn't like to be Aladdin when she gets him home tonight!

(Princess J. puts both her hands on Aladdin's shoulders, and they proceed)

Oh well, I guess that's close enough.

They reach the stage and get into position. Aladdin in front of but SL of table, Princess J in front of but SR of table, both with their backs to the audience)

HERALD:    Turn and pay your respects to your visitors from England.

( they face the audience and 'kow tow' by opening wide their arms, then stretching them above their heads, then bringing their arms down and forward as they bow deeply ).

HERALD:    Pay your respects to The Emperor and Empress.

(they 'kow tow' to them)

Face your visitors. No longer adhering to our ancient custom of the bride's parents choosing the bridegroom, you must be here of your own free will having chosen each other. Do you have any objection to this marriage?

ALADDIN:    I have no objections to this marriage.

PRINCESS J:    I have no objections to this marriage.

HERALD :    Does anyone here have objections to this marriage?

EMPEROR:    (jumping up and down)  WAAH!  He's having my baby!

WIDOW T/J:   Sit down, Eggbert!

EVERYBODY:   Sit down, Eggbert!

M U S I C # 28   "Sit Down, You're Rocking The Boat"

EVERYBODY:        For the people all said
(except           Sit down, sit down you're rockin' the boat,
Emperor)          And the people all said
                  Sit down, sit down you're rockin' the boat!

                  And the devil will drag you under
                  By the ragged ends of your satin scarf,
                  Sit down, sit down,
                  Sit down, you're rockin' the boat!

                  Sit down, sit down, sit down, sit down,
                  Sit down, you're rockin' the boat !!!

(and the Emperor reluctantly sits down - aided by Widow T/J!)

HERALD:      Ancient Chinese tradition dictates the bride must bring something red, something gold, something unique, something old.

PRINCESS J:      For something red, I bring the red veil-lifting stick, (Columbine places stick on table) for something gold, I bring the golden sword, Excalibur, (Willie W. places sword on table) for something unique, I bring the magic lamp, Blue G. places lamp on table) for something old, I bring an old tin bowl. ( Primrose trips, dropping the bowl , becoming more flustered, bumping into people trying to help, before putting the bowl on the table)

PRIMROSE:     ( tearful and agitated) I'm sorry grand Empress Lady Letitia Twankey Jingping , I didn't mean to, I get so flustered, I won't do it again, I'll try harder.

WIDOW T/J:    Foolish girl (to audience) Don't worry, I'm planning to sack her at the end of the pantomime.

(Primrose gives a little sob and sniffle and runs, getting now or when she surreptitiously can, to the rear of the stage, behind other cast members.

HERALD:        In honour of ancient times when the groom saw the bride's face for the very last time, we shall let Aladdin take the veil-lifting stick to take a peek at her face.

(the following is done with everybody knowing it is now done just for fun, so everybody laughs at Aladdin's performance)

(Aladdin takes the veil-lifting stick from the table, lifts one side of the veil, peeks underneath, recoils with horror as he pretends to be horrified) "urrgh, yuck, horrible" etc., trying not to laugh. Everybody is laughing!)

(Aladdin lifts the other side of veil, with the laughter and horror, etc)

(He and Princess J. now lift the veil over her head together, her face can be seen and he gasps with admiration at her beauty)

(Meanwhile Willie W. has exited SR and returns with 2 small teacups on a tray)

HERALD:     The proceedings will now end with the tea ceremony.

(bride and groom are each offered a cup. They face each other, clink cups three times and drink the tea, replacing cups on the tray, which Willie removes)

HERALD:     Please stand together and face your visitors. Boys and girls, mums and dad, the ancient Chinese Wedding Ceremony now completed, I present to you Sir Aladdin Abernathy Twankey and his beautiful new bride, Princess Jasmine Juniper Jingping Twankey. (they bow to the audience - perhaps a little clapping here)

You may now throw the bouquet. Ancient Chinese tradition says whoever catches the bouquet will be the next one to marry. Let us see who that one will be.

(bride and groom turn their backs to the audience. Everybody gets a little excited, a little jockeying for positions as they raise their hands to try to catch the bouquet. The bouquet is thrown an d is caught by .......Brazzadin! As the bouquet is caught he turns to face the audience, beaming with pleasure, perhaps jumping up and down with delight. Scabies S. goes all shy and giggly. They hold hands)

(everybody moves into a semi circle (handy if someone could push back the chairs and table) They should be in couples. As each couple is mentioned by name they should hold hands and smile at each other briefly)
(Primrose is at the rear, hidden behind the others. Blue G. comes to the front of the stage and addresses the audience)

BLUE G:   Boys and girls, mums and dads, your pantomime has almost ended. Aladdin is loved by the beautiful Princess Jasmine. Willie Washee is loved by the lovely handmaiden, Columbine. Grand Emperor Eggbert En-Jie Jingping is loved by the beauti ... well, his Empress Lady Letitia Twankey Jingping. Phineas Fungus is loved by Maudie Maggott. Caleb Carbuncle is loved by Daphne Dysentery. Stanley Stagnacious is loved by Priscilla Pestilence. Even Brazzadin is loved by Scabies Salmonella. In fact everybody is loved by someone. (a little sob) well, except (he now starts to sob, pulls out a handkerchief from his tunic and blows his nose ('raspberry') loudly)  I'm sorry I got upset everybody, it's just that there's never anyone in any pantomime who loves the Genie. (I'm sorry, it's just I get so lonely sometimes. I wish there was someone who loved me, but who could love a silly old Genie like me? I'm just a silly fool. (another little sob)

MUSIC # 29 "Don't Laugh At Me 'Cause I'm A Fool"

> I'm not good looking
> I'm not too smart,
> I may be foolish but I've got a heart.
>
> I know it's true, yes I'm a fool,
> No one seems to care,
> I'd give the world to share my life with someone
> Who really loves me.
>
> I see them all falling in love,
> But my lucky star hides up above.
> Some day maybe my star will shine on me,
> Don't laugh at me 'cause I'm a fool!

(gives another little sob and wipes his eyes with his handkerchief) I don't suppose I will ever find anyone who could love me, but boys and girls, mums and dads, will you look and see if you could find someone who could love me? If you ever find someone, will you just point and say "There she is!" Can you do that boys and girls, mums and dads, if you ever find someone who could love me, will you just point and say, "There she is!"

(almost at the end of his speech, Primrose starts to come forward very shyly. She raises one arm and hesitantly comes forward a little towards the left side of Blue G.)

EVERBODY:   (pointing and encouraging audience) There she is!

BLUE G:   (looking back to the right of him) You must be mistaken, I can't see anyone!

(Primrose raises one arm and hesitantly comes forward a little to the right side of Blue G.)

EVERYBODY:   (pointing and encouraging audience) There she is!

BLUE G.   (looks back to the left of him) You must be mistaken, I can't see anyone!

(Primrose raises one arm and hesitantly comes forward a little to the left side of Blue G.)

BLUE G:   (looks back to the right of him) You must be mistaken, I can't see anyone!

PRIMROSE:   (comes forward very shyly and tugs at Blue G's sleeve) I love you Blue Genie!

BLUE G:   (gasps in awe!) Oh, what a beautiful lady! Boys and girls, mums and dads, thank you so much for sending me someone so wonderful to love. I never thought I would ever find someone to love me. Now I believe something magical can happen to anyone, even me, and maybe to you!

As the following is sung, cast members, in couples, could come forward and line up in the positions they would be in, taking a curtain call.

At the Director's discretion, any cast members not in the last scene, stage hands, volunteers, anyone involved in any way, (most particularly the Director himself!) could come on, or in front of stage, to add to exuberant choruses!)

M U S I C # 30 "I'm A Believer"  (chorus, in large letters could be held up for audience to sing along)

EVERYBODY:     He thought love was only true in fairy tales,
                Meant for someone else but not for him.
                Love was out to get him,
                That's the way it seemed,
                Disappointment clouded all his dreams.

CHORUS:        Then he saw her face, now he's a believer, .......... LOUD!
                Not a trace of doubt in his mind,
                He's in love, he's a believer,
                He couldn't leave her if he tried.

                He thought love was more or less a given thing,
                Seems the more he gave the less he got,
                What's the use of trying, all you get is pain,
                When he needed sunshine, he got rain.

CHORUS:        Then he saw her face, now he's a believer.............. LOUDER!

CHORUS:        Then he saw her face, now he's a believer............. LOUDER!

BLUE G:        Boys and girls, ladies and gentlemen, you've been a wonderful audience and we hope you've enjoyed your pantomime as much as we've enjoyed performing it for you. Drive home safely and come back and see us soon, we can't wait to see you again!

(bows from everybody, hopefully lots and lots of clapping! The music has been playing softly all this time)   Boys and girls, ladies and gentlemen, let's hear it one last time!

CHORUS:        Then he saw her face, now he's a believer ............... LOUDEST!


                    CURTAIN CLOSES ............. CURTAIN CLOSED

# MUSIC LIST

(Please note: I have tried to be accurate in the information below, but I can make no guarantees. Also, it should be noted I have often not used all of the song, sometimes omitting verse, sometimes repeating choruses, etc.)

| PAGE | MUSIC | |
|---|---|---|
| 6 | # 1 | " Happy Chinese Music " Land Of China - YouTube |
| 7 | # 2 | "Swan Lake" (composed by Pyotr Ilyich Tchaikovsky in 1875-76) G: Tchaikovsky Dance Of The Swans YouTube |
| 10 | # 3 | "Bad To The Bone" (first released 1982) G: George Thorogood - Bad To The Bone YouTube. (very minor lyric alterations) |
| 11 | # 4 | "In The Navy" (Parody) (first released 1979) G: Village People In The Navy. |
| 14 | # 5 | "I Feel Pretty" (sung in West Side Story 1961) G: Julie Andrews - I Feel Pretty - YouTube" (very minor lyric alterations). |
| 16 | # 6 | "Yakety Sax Music" (first played in 1962) G: Benny Hill-Yakety Sax-YouTube |
| 17 | # 7 | "You're The One That I Want" (performed 1978) G: Grease You're The One That I Want YouTube (minor lyric alterations) |
| 18 | # 8 | "Diamonds Are A Girl's Best Friend" (1949 Musical - "Gentlemen Prefer Blonds") G: Marilyn Monroe Diamonds Are A Girl's Best Friend - YouTube (minor lyric alterations) |
| 20 | # 9 | "You're The Top" (Parody) 1934 Musical - Anything Goes G: You're The Top Ella Fitzgerald - YouTube |
| 22 | # 10 | "Till I Kissed You" (released 1959) G: The Everly Brothers - Till I Kissed You YouTube (minor lyric alterations) |
| 23 | # 11 | "Hit The Road Jack" (first recorded 1960) G: Ray Charles Hit The Road Jack (minor lyric alterations) |
| 25 | # 12 | "Scheherazade" (composed Nikolai Rimsky Korsakov 1888) G: ancient Arabian music Scheherazade. |

## LIGHTING AND SOUND EFECTS

PAGE     ACT 1     Scene 1

9     Sound of distant thunder
     Large sound of thunder and/or cymbals/flash of light/lights out for 2 or 3 secs.

13     Sound of trumpets
13     More trumpets
13     More trumpets

14     Loud sound of trumpets

23     Clap of thunder and/or cymbals/light flashes/lights go out for a few seconds.


     ACT 1     Scene 2

27     Clap of thunder and/or cymbals/3 secs. Darkness/flash of light

29     Lights go out briefly, clash of cymbals/flash of blue light

33     Clap of thunder and/or cymbals/3secs. Of darkness/flash of light

34     Loud dragon roar
34     Even louder dragon roar
34     Even louder dragon roar

35     Clash of cymbals, 2 secs. Darkness/flash of blue light
35     Loud roaring dragon sound

36     Thunder and/or cymbals/lights out for 2 secs/flash of blue light
36     Loudest fearsome dragon roar
36     Buzzing sound

38     Louder Bzzz Bzzz Bzzz
38     Even louder Bzzz Bzzz Bzzz
38     Loudest Bzzz Bzzz Bzzz

39     Clash of cymbals/lights out 2 secs/flash of blue light
39     Loudest Bzzz Bzzz Bzzz

41     Roaring sound (G: grizzly bear roar YouTube)
41     Louder roar
41     Even louder roar
41     Clash of cymbals/2 secs darkness/flash of blue light
41     Loudest roar

| | |
|---|---|
| 42 | thunder and/or cymbals/lights out for 2 secs/flash of blue light |
| 44 | Roaring sound (lions roaring sound) |
| 44 | Louder roar |
| 44 | Loudest roar |
| 45 | Clash of cymbals/lights out 2 secs/flash of blue light |
| 45 | Another loudest roar |
| 46 | Thunder and/or cymbals, lights go out for a few seconds/flash of blue light |

ACT 2       Scene 1

| | |
|---|---|
| 49 | Dim lighting, brightening as scene progresses |
| 49 | Yellow/gold spotlight illuminating sword |
| 51 | Clap of thunder and/or cymbals/light flashes/lights out for a few secs. |
| 54 | thunder clap and/or cymbals, light flashes/lights go out for a few seconds |
| 55 | A clap of thunder/flash of (red?) light |
| 58 | A little clash of cymbals and blue light |

ACT 2       Scene 2

| | |
|---|---|
| 60 | Knock at the door (big bangs, knocks, etc) |

---

# PROPS LIST

| PAGE | ACT 1 | Scene 1 |
|------|-------|---------|

| | |
|-----|-----|
| 6 | Table or counter |
| 6 | Simple wooden chair |
| 6 | Optional: clothes containers/fake washing machine/mangle/washboards/filled Clothes line/old clothes |
| 6 | Willie W.  mop or broom |
| 6 | Widow T.  long loaf of 'bread' reinforced on underside. |
| 8 | Primrose  tin bowl(s) or similar |
| 12 | Large orange knickers |
| 12 | Large red bloomers |
| 13 | Widow T.  large red bloomers |
| 14 | Widow T.  large hand 'mirror' bright red lipstick |
| 14 | Optional: sedan chair |
| 16 | Emperor:  hilariously decorated boxer shorts and undershirt, slip on shoes/ Long scarf |
| 19/20 | Princess J.  bag from Waitrose, Sainsbury or Ocada Hairbrush, box of chocolates, red rose |
| 19/20 | Columbine  Bag from Lidl or Asda Toothbrush, rotting potato, mouldy carrot |

ACT 1        Scene 2

| | |
|-----|-----|
| 25 | Tramp  old hat, carpet bag or similar, the 'magic' lamp |
| 26 | Aladdin  the long thin loaf of 'bread' |
| 29 | Blue G.  plain 'hamburger bun' |
| 32 | Lenny  small notebook and pencil |
| 36 | Blue G.  water spray bottle |
| 36 | Puffley    Blow out |

| 40 | Blue G. | fly swatter |
|----|---------|-------------|
| 40 | Puffley | Green nail varnish (if hands show outside costume) |
| 42 | Blue G. | Feather duster |
| 46 | Blue G. | Blue G. large pair of pliers |
| 47 | Optional: | Something for Aladdin to sit upon |
| 47 | Aladdin: | large white handkerchief |
| 47 | Leopold: | Large 'thorn' |

ACT 2     Scene 1

| 49 | Golden sword 'embedded' in a rock |
|----|-----------------------------------|
| 55 | Widow T/J   Large, grubby, rag |
| 56/57 | Widow T/J   2 large 'diamond' rings |

ACT 2     Scene 2

| 60 | any possible red/gold decoration G: Our Traditional Chinese Wedding - full version |
|----|-----------------------------------------------------------------------------------|
| 60 | Table or counter covered with red/gold cloth |
| 60 | 2 'royal' chairs |

| 61 | Wilie W. | red envelope |
|----|----------|--------------|
| 61 | 'Creatures' | newspaper 'money' |
| 61 | Columbine | red stick |
| 61 | Blue G. | 'magic' lamp |
| 61 | Willie W. | the golden sword |
| 61 | Primrose | small tin bowl |
| 61 | Princess J. | red veil, red kimono for her and possibly Aladdin |

| 64 | Blue G. | handkerchief |
|----|---------|--------------|